MATH AND GRAPHING SKILLS

Copyright © 2008 Pacific Crest

ISBN 987-1-60263-596-8

by   Betty Lawrence, SUNY Empire State College

Kathleen Burke, SUNY Cortland

Denna Hintze, Pacific Crest

Cover by Denna Hintze, Pacific Crest

Purpose of this book

Welcome to Math and Graphing Skills. The purpose of this book is to give you a non-threatening environment for evaluating your quantitative skills.

While this book is not intended to serve as a textbook, it can be used to remind you of some techniques and ideas that you may have learned at another point in your life. Each module contains some explanations, some things to remember and a few examples. It also contains critical thinking questions to help you reflect on the principles involved.

Using a calculator?

Most modules should be completed without a calculator. Your should check with your instructor; he/she may decide that use of a calculator is appropriate for some modules.

CONTENTS

BUILDING UNDERSTANDING

A *natural number* is any positive integer, or counting number {1, 2, 3, 4, 5, ...}

You can visualize the adding of natural numbers with more than one digit by picturing an odometer on the dashboard of a car.

Suppose we start out with an odometer reading of 153 miles. We then proceed to drive. For the first 6 miles, the odometer's rightmost digit increases by one for each mile driven. We would write this as 153 + 6 = 159.

| 1 | 5 | 3 |

| 1 | 5 | 9 |

When we reach 159 miles and continue to drive for another mile, the odometer's rightmost digit goes from 9 to 0 and the middle digit increases by one to 6. Therefore, 159 + 1 = 160.

| 1 | 6 | 0 |

 THINGS TO REMEMBER

When adding columns of numbers, if the sum of a column is greater than 9, use only the "units" value, and *carry* the "tens" value to the next column.

 MODELS

```
  1 1
  378      Column 1: 8 + 3 = 11 (carry 1)
+ 483      Column 2: 7 + 8 + 1 = 16 (carry 1)
  861      Column 3: 3 + 4 + 1 = 8
```

```
   1
  695
+ 783
 1478
```

? **CRITICAL THINKING QUESTIONS**

1. What is meant by *carrying* when adding numbers?

2. Why is it easier to add numbers containing multiple digits in vertical columns rather than horizontally?

3. What can you do to validate your answers to make sure they are correct?

NATURAL NUMBER SUBTRACTION

BUILDING UNDERSTANDING

A *natural number* is any positive integer, or counting number {1, 2, 3, 4, 5, ...}

The odometer on a car dashboard is also a good model for helping you visualize the subtracting of natural numbers with more than one digit. In this case, subtracting can be viewed as driving a car in reverse with the numbers turning in the reverse direction (decreasing).

Suppose the odometer reading is 248 miles. As we drive in reverse, the odometer's rightmost digit decreases by one for every mile driven. The rightmost digit continues to decrease from eight until zero is reached. So, 248 – 8 = 240.

| 2 | 4 | 8 |

| 2 | 4 | 0 |

| 2 | 3 | 9 |

When we reach 240 miles and continue to drive in reverse for another mile, the odometer's rightmost digit goes from 0 to 9 and the middle and the middle digit decreases by one to 3. In a sense, we have "borrowed" from the ten's column to do the subtraction in the one's column. This is written as 240 – 1 = 239.

THINGS TO REMEMBER

When subtracting columns of numbers, if the bottom digit is larger than the top digit, *borrow* from the next column.

◣● MODELS

$$
\begin{array}{r}
{\scriptstyle 4\ 11} \\
\not{5}1 \\
-\ 23 \\
\hline
28
\end{array}
$$
Column 1: 3 is larger than 1
Borrow from Column 2: 11 – 3 = 8
Column 2: 4 – 2 = 2

$$
\begin{array}{r}
{\scriptstyle 4\ 12} \\
5\not{5}2 \\
-\ 436 \\
\hline
116
\end{array}
$$

❓ CRITICAL THINKING QUESTIONS

1. What is meant by *borrowing* when subtracting numbers?

2. What should you do to validate that your answer is correct?

BUILDING UNDERSTANDING

Multiplication is the process of repeated addition. For example, if we have 6 boxes of compact disks with 12 disks in each box, we would have a total of 72 compact disks. This can be represented in the following manner:

6 × 12 = 12 + 12 + 12 + 12 + 12 + 12 = 72

An important aid for multiplication is the following table of multiplication facts:

Mult (×)	1	2	3	4	5	6	7	8	9
1	1	2	3	4	5	6	7	8	9
2	2	4	6	8	10	12	14	16	18
3	3	6	9	12	15	18	21	24	27
4	4	8	12	16	20	24	28	32	36
5	5	10	15	20	25	30	35	40	45
6	6	12	18	24	30	36	42	48	54
7	7	14	21	28	35	42	49	56	63
8	8	16	24	32	40	48	56	64	72
9	9	18	27	36	45	54	63	72	81

You should have these multiplication facts memorized; the best way to remember them is by using them. Also, review the table carefully to see what helpful trends there are. For example, what about multiples of 5? Do you notice anything special about multiples of 9?

 THINGS TO REMEMBER

- If you are multiplying a number with more than one digit, multiply each decimal column or place separately. *Carry* any "tens" digit to the next column. See the following examples.

- If you are multiplying two numbers each with more than one digit (e.g., **22 × 34**), after multiplying by the "ones" digit, remember to account for multiplication by the "tens" digit by writing down the product of the tens digit with a zero in the rightmost column before starting to multiply.

```
        22
    ×   34
    ───────
        88
  +   660   ← place a zero in the one's column before multiplying
    ───────
       748
```

Recall that multiplication in this module is limited to natural numbers (positive integers).

$$\begin{array}{r} 4\ 2 \\ 3 6 4 \\ \times\ \ 7 \\ \hline 2 5 4 8 \end{array}$$

7 × 4 = 28   (put 8 in the *ones* column and carry 2)

7 × 6 + 2 = 42 + 2 = 44   (put the 4 in the *tens* column and carry 4)

(7 × 3) + 4 = 21 + 4 = 25   (put 5 in the *hundreds* column and 2 in the *thousands*)

$$\begin{array}{r} 2 8 \\ \times\ 4 6 \\ \hline 1 6 8 \\ +\ 1 1 2 0 \\ \hline 1 2 8 8 \end{array}$$

6 × 8 = 48   (put 8 in the *ones* column and carry 4)

(6 × 2) + 4 = 12 + 4 = 16   (put 6 in the *tens* column and 1 in the *hundreds*)

Remember to place a 0 in the "ones" column before doing the products from the ten's digit!

4 × 8 = 32   (put 2 in the *tens* column and carry 3)

(4 × 2) + 3 = 11   (put 1 in the *hundreds* column and 1 in the *thousands*)

? CRITICAL THINKING QUESTIONS

1. Why is multiplication called the process of repeated addition?

2. What is meant by the term *carrying*?

3. How can you validate that the result of your multiplication is correct?

BUILDING UNDERSTANDING

Division is the process of finding how many times a number (*the divisor*) is contained in a number (*the dividend*); the number of times equals the **quotient**. For example:

D = Dividend

Q = Quotient

DV = Divisor

$$108 \div 12 = 9$$
$$\text{(D)} \quad \text{(DV)} \quad \text{(Q)}$$

$$546 / 26 = 21$$
$$\text{(D)} \quad \text{(DV)} \quad \text{(Q)}$$

$$\text{(Q)}$$
$$\text{(DV)} \quad 7\overline{)70}^{\,10}$$
$$\text{(D)}$$

$$\text{(D)} \frac{30}{5} = 6 \text{(Q)}$$
$$\text{(DV)}$$

Consider a situation where 8 people want to share 3 medium-sized pizzas. How much does each person get? If each pizza is divided into 8 slices, there are 24 slices total, shared among 8 people: $24 \div 8 = 3$. Each person gets 3 slices.

When the divisor does not divide evenly into a dividend, the quotient will have a **remainder**. A remainder is what is left over when one number does not divide evenly into another. In the pizza example, we had no leftovers and thus no remainder.

Consider $55 \div 4$. Since 4 is not a factor of 55 (4 does not divide evenly into 55), the quotient will have a remainder. In this case, the remainder is 3.

The remainder can be expressed as a fraction: $\frac{3}{4}$, or as a decimal: 0.75.

$$
\begin{array}{r}
13 \quad \textit{remainder 3} \\
4\overline{)55} \\
\underline{4} \\
15 \\
\underline{12} \\
3
\end{array}
$$

 ## THINGS TO REMEMBER

When the divisor does not divide evenly into a dividend then the quotient will have a remainder. The remainder can be expressed as a remainder, or it can be converted into a fractional or decimal equivalent.

For example, $89 \div 5 = 17$ with a remainder of 4. Check it: ($17 \times 5 = 85$, $8 + 4 = 89$)

A remainder of 4 with a divisor of 5 gives a fraction of $\frac{4}{5}$ or 0.80 in decimal form.

Therefore, $89 \div 5 = 17$ *remainder* 4, or $17\frac{4}{5} = 17.80$

Divide the following. If the divisor does not divide evenly into the dividend, write the quotient with a remainder.

$$643 \div 20 = 20\overline{)643} \quad \overset{32 \ \ rem\,3}{}$$
$$\underline{60}$$
$$43$$
$$\underline{40}$$
$$3$$

$$741 \div 11 = 11\overline{)741} \quad \overset{67 \ \ rem\,4}{}$$
$$\underline{66}$$
$$81$$
$$\underline{77}$$
$$4$$

$$476 \div 19 = 19\overline{)476} \quad \overset{25 \ \ rem\,1}{}$$
$$\underline{38}$$
$$96$$
$$\underline{95}$$
$$1$$

$$585 \div 21 = 21\overline{)585} \quad \overset{27 \ \ rem\,18}{}$$
$$\underline{42}$$
$$165$$
$$\underline{147}$$
$$18$$

$$236 \div 13 = 13\overline{)236} \quad \overset{18 \ \ rem\,2}{}$$
$$\underline{13}$$
$$106$$
$$\underline{104}$$
$$2$$

? CRITICAL THINKING QUESTIONS

1. What are three different ways to write the expression, "eighty divided by twenty"?

2. What is the difference between a divisor and a dividend?

3. When will a quotient have a remainder and when will it not?

4. Can a remainder ever be larger than a divisor? Explain your answer.

BUILDING UNDERSTANDING

Integer addition and subtraction can be pictured as a game of tug-of-war. Unlike the natural numbers (1, 2, 3, ...), *integers* also include negative numbers and the number 0: {... –3, –2, –1, 0, 1, 2, 3, 4 ...}

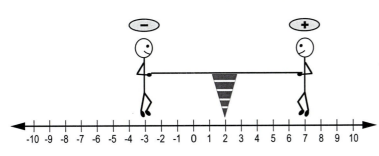

The contestants in this game are "Plus" to the right and "Minus" to the left. At the start of the game, the flag rests over the "0" mark on the number line.

Let's illustrate the following: (+2) + (–3) = –1

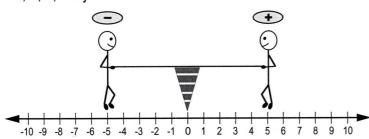

First, "Plus" pulls 2, moving the flag to the +2 position.

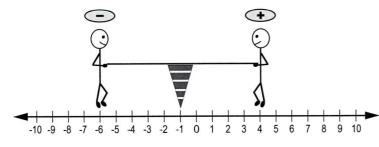

Then "Minus" pulls 3, moving the flag to the –1 position.

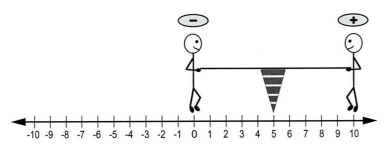

Now what if "Minus" didn't pull in the usual direction, but pushed (moving the flag to the right)?

The result of "Minus" moving forward 3 moves the flag to +5.

We see that + 2 – (–3) = + 5.

This is the same result as "Plus" pulling + 3. Therefore, 2 – (–3) = 2 + 3 = 5.

The tug-of-war model can be used for any addition problem. The sign of the numbers involved determines the team that is pulling. If *subtraction* occurs, the team *pushes* (moving the flag in the opposite of its usual direction).

THINGS TO REMEMBER

Here are some important rules:

$$-(-a) = +a \qquad\qquad -(-3) = 3$$

$$a + 0 = a \qquad\qquad 5 + 0 = 5$$

$$a + (-a) = 0 \qquad\qquad 4 + (-4) = 0$$

$$a + b = b + a \qquad\qquad 6 + 2 = 2 + 6 \qquad (8 = 8)$$

$$a + (-b) = a - b \qquad\qquad 7 + (-3) = 7 - 3 \qquad (4 = 4)$$

$$-a + b = b - a \qquad\qquad -3 + 5 = 5 - 3$$

MODELS

$$5 + 4 - (-8) = 9 + 8 = 17 \qquad\qquad -7 - (-4) - 2 = -7 + 4 - 2 = -3 - 2 = -5$$

$$8 - (-5) + (-10) = 8 + 5 - 10 = 13 - 10 = 3 \qquad\qquad -2 - 1 + 3 = -3 + 3 = 0$$

 ## CRITICAL THINKING QUESTIONS

1. Does it matter in which order you add two integers? Explain.

2. When you add two negative integers together, what do you know about the answer?

3. When you add a positive integer with a negative integer, how do you know if the answer is positive or negative?

4. What are three important rules of integer addition and subtraction you can share to help someone correctly add any set of integers?

BUILDING UNDERSTANDING

This module is about integer multiplication and division and is very similar to the modules about natural number multiplication and division, except that negative numbers are now included. If you apply what you know about multiplication and division, this module will require to you determine how to use signs (positive or negative) correctly when multiplying and dividing positive and negative integers.

Multiplying or Dividing Positive and Negative Numbers

*   When two negative numbers are multiplied or divided, the result is a positive number.

*   When a positive and a negative number are multiplied or divided the result is a negative number.

THINGS TO REMEMBER

This module differs from the Natural Number Multiplication and Addition modules in that negative numbers are introduced and the quotients from division will have no remainder.

Concepts assume that the denominators are non-zero. Division by zero is not defined.

Concept		Example
$a \times 0 = 0$	Property of zero	$0 \times 7 = 0$
$\dfrac{0}{a} = 0$	Rule of zero	$\dfrac{0}{28} = 0$
$a \times 1 = a$	Multiplicative identity	$14 \times 1 = 14$
$\dfrac{a}{1} = a$	Division by one	$\dfrac{20}{1} = 20$
$a \times b = b \times a$ $a \times -b = -b \times a$	Commutative property	$14 \times 6 = 6 \times 14 \quad (84 = 84)$ $3 \times -15 = -15 \times 3 \quad (-45 = -45)$
$-a \times -b = +(a \times b)$	Negative times a negative equals a positive	$-9 \times -4 = +(9 \times 4) = +36$
$\dfrac{-a}{-b} = +\dfrac{a}{b}$	Negative divided by a negative equals a positive	$\dfrac{-60}{-4} = +\dfrac{60}{4} = +15$
$-a \times b = -(a \times b)$	Negative times a positive equals a negative	$-2 \times 12 = -(2 \times 12) = -24$
$\dfrac{-a}{b} = -\dfrac{a}{b}$	Negative divided by a positive equals a negative	$\dfrac{-36}{12} = -\dfrac{36}{12} = -4$

Note: When multiplying and dividing positive and negative numbers, first perform the multiplication (and arrive at the product) or division (and arrive at the quotient) as if all the numbers are positive. Then go back and apply the appropriate sign (positive or negative) to the result, based on the signs of the original numbers.

 ## MODELS

The important aspect of Integer Multiplication and Division is that you determine the correct sign of the answer.

$$(-2) \times (-3) \times (-5) = 6 \times (-5) = -30$$

$$7 \times (-8) \div 2 = -56 \div 2 = -28$$

$$(-6) \div (-2) \times (-4) = 3 \times -4 = -12$$

? CRITICAL THINKING QUESTIONS

1. What is always the result of multiplying a number by zero?

2. What can you say about multiplying or dividing a number by one?

3. Does the order in which numbers are multiplied make a difference? Explain.

4. What is the outcome of multiplying or dividing a positive number by a negative number?

5. What is the outcome of multiplying or dividing a negative number by a negative number?

BUILDING UNDERSTANDING

Factoring a natural number involves finding the integers that, when multiplied together, equal that natural number.

A natural number is said to be *prime* when the only integers involved in the process of factoring that number are 1 and the number itself. Examples of prime numbers include: 2, 3, 5, 7, and 11.

The *prime factors* of a natural number is the collection of prime numbers which, when multiplied together, equal that natural number. For example, the prime factors of 30 are as follows:

$$30 = 2 \times 3 \times 5$$

METHODOLOGY

One method of factoring is to use a *factor tree*.

1. Put the number to be factored at the top.

2. Factor the number into the product of two integers and put each one on the "branch" below.

   a) If the number is prime, circle it, (letter A). *That branch is complete.*

   b) If the number is not prime, put a square around it (letter B). Factor this number into the product of two integers and put each one on the "branch" below (letters C and D).

   c) Continue until there are only prime factors (circles) left (letters C and D).

 ## THINGS TO REMEMBER

1. The first ten prime numbers are: 2, 3, 5, 7, 11, 13, 17, 19, 23, and 29.

2. If a number is even, the integer "2" will be a factor at least once:

$$16 = 2 \times 8$$
$$= 2 \times 2 \times 4$$
$$= 2 \times 2 \times 2 \times 2$$

3. If the sum of the digits of a number can be divided by 3, then the number can be divided by 3 and therefore, 3 will be a factor at least once.

126   (sum of the digits is 1 + 2 + 6 = 9 which is divisible by 3)

$126 = 3 \times 42$ (42, sum of the digits is 4 + 2 = 6 which is divisible by 3)

$126 = 3 \times 3 \times 14$

$126 = 3 \times 3 \times 2 \times 7$ *final prime factorization of 126*

4. Numbers that have 0 and 5 for the last digit (except 0) are divisible by 5; therefore, five will be a factor at least once.

$$140 = 10 \times 14 \qquad\qquad 65 = 5 \times 13$$
$$140 = 2 \times 5 \times 2 \times 7$$

  MODELS

Factor the following natural numbers:

$196 = 2 \times 98$
$\qquad = 2 \times 2 \times 49$
$\qquad = 2 \times 2 \times 7 \times 7$

$36 = 3 \times 12$
$\quad = 3 \times 3 \times 4$
$\quad = 3 \times 3 \times 2 \times 2$

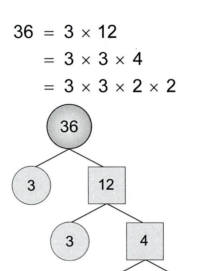

$3150 = 10 \times 315$
$\qquad = 2 \times 5 \times 5 \times 63$
$\qquad = 2 \times 5 \times 5 \times 7 \times 9$
$\qquad = 2 \times 5 \times 5 \times 7 \times 3 \times 3$

$175 = 5 \times 35$
$\qquad = 5 \times 5 \times 7$

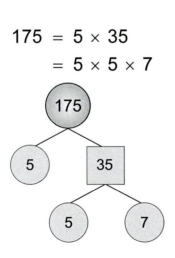

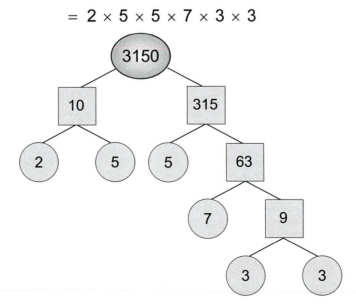

Math and Graphing Skills

1. How can you tell if a number is prime?

2. What are the easiest factors to look for first?

3. How can you tell if a number is divisible by 5? by 3?

4. Does it matter in what order you find the factors? Explain.

5. How can you determine the largest prime number you should try dividing into your number?

BUILDING UNDERSTANDING

A *multiple* is a number that is a product of some specified number and another number. For example, 10 is a multiple of 5 because 5 (*specified number*) times 2 (*another number*) produces 10 (*multiple*).

A *common multiple* is a multiple of more than one number. For example, 48 is a multiple of 8 (8 × 6), and 48 is a multiple of 12 (4 × 12). Therefore, 48 is one common multiple of both 8 and 12. However, 8 and 12 have other common multiples including 24, 72, 96, 120, and so on.

The smallest common multiple of two numbers is called their *least common multiple* (LCM). The least common multiple of 8 and 12 is 24. In other words, 24 is the smallest number which can be evenly divided by both 8 and 12.

METHODOLOGY

The following is a method for finding the least common multiple of two numbers. It involves finding the prime factors for each number and placing these factors into a table where it becomes easy to determine which numbers are to be used to calculate the least common multiple.

To Find the Least Common Multiple (LCM):

1. Determine the prime factors for each number. Refer to the previous module "Factoring Natural Numbers" for more information.

2. Create the following table.

	prime number #1	prime number #2	prime number #3	*continue*
first number	# of occurrences	# of occurrences	# of occurrences	
second number	# of occurrences	# of occurrences	# of occurrences	
most occurrences	most occurrences (A)	most occurrences (B)	most occurrences (C)	
list of primes	prime #1 A times	prime #2 B times	prime #3 C times	

a) Place the numbers for which we are finding the LCM in the first column.

b) List all the prime numbers that are factors for the numbers in the first column. Place each prime number at the top of a column.

c) Under each prime number, indicate how many times that prime number is used when factoring each number in the first column. *Note: in some cases, a prime number will appear as a factor for one number but not the other.*

d) In the row titled "most occurrences," write down the largest number of occurrences in that column. This represents the greatest number of occurrences of that particular prime number.

e) In the row, "list of primes," write each prime number a certain number of times: the most occurrences from the previous row (A times for prime # 1, B times for prime #2, etc.)

3. Calculate the LCM.

a) Multiply all the numbers in the row "list of primes." The product of all these numbers is the least common multiple.

Note: this table can be used to determine the LCM for more than two numbers.

 MODELS

Find the least common multiple for the following

LCM for 10 and 12:

Prime factors for each number are: 10 = 2 × 5 and 12 = 2 × 2 × 3

	prime number: 2	prime number: 3	prime number: 5
first number: 10	1 occurrence	0 occurrences	1 occurrence
second number: 12	2 occurrences	1 occurrence	0 occurrences
most occurrences	2	1	1
list of primes	2, 2	3	5

LCM = 2 × 2 × 3 × 5 = 4 × 15 = 60

LCM for 20 and 75:

Prime factors for each number are: 20 = 2 × 2 × 5 and 75 = 3 × 5 × 5

	prime number: 2	prime number: 3	prime number: 5
first number: 20	2 occurrences	0 occurrences	1 occurrence
second number: 75	0 occurrences	1 occurrence	2 occurrences
most occurrences	2	1	2
list of primes	2, 2	3	5, 5

LCM = 2 × 2 × 3 × 5 × 5 = 4 × 15 × 5 = 60 × 5 = 300

LCM for 126 and 210:

Prime factors for each number are: 126 = 2 × 3 × 3 × 7 and 210 = 2 × 3 × 5 × 7

	prime number: 2	prime number: 3	prime number: 5	prime number: 7
first number: 126	1 occurrence	2 occurrences	0 occurrences	1 occurrence
second number: 210	1 occurrences	1 occurrences	1 occurrence	1 occurrence
most occurrences	1	2	1	1
list of primes	2	3, 3	5	7

LCM = 2 × 3 × 3 × 5 × 7 = 2 × 9 × 35 = 18 × 35 = 630

1. What is the difference between a common multiple and a least common multiple?

2. What is the least common multiple of two prime numbers?

3. Can the LCM of a set of numbers be smaller than any of the numbers? Why?

4. Must the LCM of a set of numbers be evenly divisible by all the factors of each? Why?

5. How can you validate that the LCM you have found is correct?

6. How many least common multiples can two numbers have? How many common multiples?

MODULE 9 | # GREATEST COMMON DIVISOR

 ## BUILDING UNDERSTANDING

A *divisor* is a number or quantity by which a dividend is divided to produce a quotient. In the situation where 50 is to be divided by 10, 50 is the *dividend*, 10 is the *divisor* and 5 is the *quotient*.

A *common divisor* is a divisor of more than one number. For example, 4 is a divisor of 48 (48 ÷ 4 = 12) and 4 is also a divisor of 36 (36 ÷ 4 = 9). Therefore, 4 is one common divisor for 48 and 36. However, 48 and 36 have other common divisors including 2, 6, and 12.

The largest common divisor of two numbers is called their *greatest common divisor* (GCD). The greatest common divisor of 48 and 36 is 12. In other words, 12 is the largest number than can be evenly divided into both 48 and 36.

 ## METHODOLOGY

The following is a method for finding the greatest common divisor of two numbers. It involves finding the prime factors for each number and placing these factors into a table where it becomes easy to determine which numbers are to be used to calculate the greatest common divisor.

To Find the Greatest Common Divisor (GCD):

1. Determine the prime factors for each number. Refer to the previous module "Factoring Natural Numbers" for more information.

2. Create the following table.

	prime number #1	prime number #2	prime number #3	continue with as many prime numbers as there are for the numbers
first number	list all occurrences	list all occurrences	list all occurrences	
second number	list all occurrences	list all occurrences	list all occurrences	
common occurrences	list all common occurrences	list all common occurrences	list all common occurrences	

   a) Place the numbers for which we are finding the GCD in the first column.

   b) List all the prime numbers that are factors for the numbers in the first column. Place each prime number at the top of a column.

   c) Under each prime number, list all occurrences of that prime number when factoring each number in the first column.

   d) In the row titled "common occurrences," list all the common occurrences of prime numbers. This represents the greatest number of occurrences of that particular prime number.

3. Calculate the greatest common divisor by multiplying all the prime numbers that are listed in the "common occurrences" row. The product of these numbers is the GCD.

Find the greatest common divisor for the following pairs of numbers.

GCD for 10 and 12:

Prime factors for each number are: 10 = 2 × 5   and   12 = 2 × 2 × 3

	prime number: 2	prime number: 3	prime number: 5
first number: 10	2		5
second number: 12	2, 2	3	
common occurrences	2		

GCD = 2

GCD for 30 and 45:

Prime factors for each number are: 30 = 2 × 3 × 5   and   45 = 3 × 3 × 5

	prime number: 2	prime number: 3	prime number: 5
first number: 30	2	3	5
second number: 45		3, 3	5
common occurrences		3	5

GCD = 3 × 5 = 15

GCD for 27 and 45:

Prime factors for each number are: 27 = 3 × 3 × 3   and   45 = 3 × 3 × 5

	prime number: 3	prime number: 5
first number: 27	3, 3, 3	
second number: 45	3, 3	5
common occurrences	3, 3	

GCD = 3 × 3 = 9

GCD for 126 and 315:

Prime factors for each number are: 126 = 2 × 3 × 3 × 7   and   315 = 3 × 3 × 5 × 7

	prime number: 2	prime number: 3	prime number: 5	prime number: 7
first number: 126	2	3, 3		7
second number: 315		3, 3	5	7
common occurrences		3, 3		7

GCD = 3 × 3 × 7 = 9 × 7 = 63

1. What does it mean for a number to be the greatest common divisor of two numbers?

2. What is the difference between a common divisor and a greatest common divisor?

3. Can the GCD of a set of numbers be larger than any of the numbers? Why?

4. Must all the factors for every number in a set of numbers be evenly divisible by the GCD? Why?

5. How can you validate that the GCD you've found is correct?

MODULE 10 ADDING AND SUBTRACTING FRACTIONS

BUILDING UNDERSTANDING

When adding or subtracting fractions, you will encounter two possible situations: either the fractions have a common denominator (like fractions) or the denominators are different (unlike fractions).

To add or subtract fractions with common denominators:

1. Add or subtract the numerators.
2. Place the sum or difference of the numerators over the common denominator.
3. Simplify the fraction to its lowest terms.

$$\text{For example, } \frac{2}{3} + \frac{4}{3} = \frac{6}{3} = 2$$

In the case of different denominators, the fractions must be converted so that a common denominator exists. The **least common denominator** is the *least common multiple of all the denominators*.

In this module you will need to use your knowledge about prime factorization and least common multiples (refer to previous modules for more information about these topics if necessary).

METHODOLOGY

Below is a series of steps that you can use in adding or subtracting fractions which have different denominators. You are not required to use these steps, but you may find them helpful in the beginning. You will use the process of prime factorization and finding least common multiples to create a least common denominator, change the numerators to their new equivalents, and ultimately calculate a final fractional answer.

The seven (7) steps are as follows:

1. Find the prime factors of the first denominator.
2. Find the prime factors of the second denominator.
3. Using the information from steps 1 and 2, find the prime factors of the least common denominator.
4. Multiply the numerator and denominator of the first fraction by whatever is needed to get the least common denominator in the denominator.
5. Multiply the numerator and denominator of the second fraction by whatever is needed to get the least common denominator in the denominator.
6. Now, you should have two fractions with the same denominator. Add or subtract these fractions as indicated.
7. Often, this answer can be reduced. Divide top and bottom by any common factors as necessary.

MODELS

Add or subtract the following fractions as required.

$$\frac{7}{10} - \frac{4}{6}$$

Steps		
1	Find the prime factors of the first denominator.	$10 = 2 \times 5$
2	Find the prime factors of the second denominator.	$6 = 2 \times 3$
3	Using the information from 1 and 2, find the prime factors of the least common denominator.	$LCD = 30 \quad 30 = 2 \times 3 \times 5$
4	Multiply the numerator and denominator of the first fraction by whatever is needed to get the least common denominator in the denominator.	Multiply $\frac{7}{10}$ by $\frac{3}{3}$ to get $\frac{21}{30}$
5	Multiply the numerator and denominator of the second fraction by whatever is needed to get the least common denominator in the denominator.	Multiply $\frac{4}{6}$ by $\frac{5}{5}$ to get $\frac{20}{30}$
6	Now, you should have two fractions with the same denominator. Add or subtract these Fractions as indicated.	$\frac{21}{30} - \frac{20}{30} = \frac{1}{30}$
7	This answer can often be reduced. Divide top and bottom by any common factors as necessary.	This answer is in final form (it cannot be reduced further).

$$\frac{5}{3} - \frac{8}{20}$$

Steps			
1	Find the prime factors of the first denominator.	$3 = 1 \times 3$	
2	Find the prime factors of the second denominator.	$20 = 2 \times 2 \times 5$	
3	Using the information from 1 and 2, find the prime factors of the least common denominator.	$LCD = 60 \quad 60 = 2 \times 2 \times 3 \times 5$	
4	Multiply the numerator and denominator of the first fraction by whatever is needed to get the least common denominator in the denominator.	Multiply $\frac{5}{3}$ by $\frac{20}{20}$ to get $\frac{100}{60}$	
5	Multiply the numerator and denominator of the second fraction by whatever is needed to get the least common denominator in the denominator.	Multiply $\frac{8}{20}$ by $\frac{3}{3}$ to get $\frac{24}{60}$	
6	Now, you should have two fractions with the same denominator. Add or subtract these Fractions as indicated.	$\frac{100}{60} - \frac{24}{60} = \frac{76}{60}$	
7	This answer can often be reduced. Divide top and bottom by any common factors as necessary.	76 and 60 are both divisible by 4:	$\frac{76 \div 4}{60 \div 4} = \frac{19}{15}$

THINGS TO REMEMBER

The least common denominator is the least common multiple of all the denominators.

Look to cancel common factors in your final steps. This will ensure that the final answer is reduced to the lowest possible terms.

CRITICAL THINKING QUESTIONS

1. Why is it necessary to create a common denominator when fractions have different or unlike denominators?

2. What is meant by *least common denominator*?

3. How do you calculate or determine the least common denominator?

4. What does the process of cancellation involve?

5. How does the use of prime factors help to ensure that the final answer is reduced to lowest terms?

6. How can you validate your final answer?

MULTIPLYING AND DIVIDING FRACTIONS

BUILDING UNDERSTANDING

Recall that multiplication of natural numbers was described as the process of repeated addition:

$$3 + 3 + 3 + 3 + 3 = 5 \times 3 = 15$$

Multiplication of fractions can be viewed in a similar manner:

$$4 \times \frac{1}{5} = \frac{1}{5} + \frac{1}{5} + \frac{1}{5} + \frac{1}{5} = \frac{4}{5}$$ so that in fractional form: $\frac{4}{1} \times \frac{1}{5} = \frac{4}{5}$

As a general rule, **when multiplying two or more fractions**, the *numerator* is calculated by multiplying the numerators of the fractions and the *denominator* is calculated by multiplying the denominators of the fractions.

The *reciprocal* of a number is its multiplicative inverse, and a number multiplied by its multiplicative inverse is equal to one. For example, 2 is the reciprocal of 1/2, and 3/4 is the reciprocal of 4/3.

When **dividing two fractions**, *multiply* the first fraction by the reciprocal of the second.

 ## METHODOLOGY

To Multiply Fractions:	To Divide Fractions:
1. Put all numbers in fractional form.	1. Put all numbers in fractional form.
2. Multiply numerators (A × C) to calculate the numerator.	2. Take the reciprocal of the second fraction (the divisor).
3. Multiply denominators (B × D) to calculate the denominator.	3. Change the sign to multiplication and multiply the first fraction (the dividend) by the reciprocal of the second fraction.
4. Simplify the resulting fraction to its lowest terms by dividing out the Greatest Common Factor of the numerator and denominator. $$\frac{a}{b} \times \frac{c}{d} = \frac{a \times c}{b \times d}$$	4. Simplify the resulting fraction to its lowest terms by dividing out the Greatest Common Factor of the numerator and denominator. $$\frac{a}{b} \div \frac{c}{d} = \frac{a \times d}{b \times c}$$
Example:	Example:
$$\frac{5}{7} \times \frac{3}{8} = \frac{5 \times 3}{7 \times 8} = \frac{15}{56}$$	$$\frac{3}{4} \div \frac{6}{5} = \frac{3 \times 5}{4 \times 6} = \frac{15}{24} = \frac{5}{8}$$

THINGS TO REMEMBER

When fractions are multiplied, look to use the process of cancellation to simplify the numbers you must multiply. Cancellation involves finding a number greater than zero that can be evenly divided into both the numerator and the denominator. For example:

$$\frac{\cancel{3}}{5} \times \frac{2}{\cancel{3}} = \frac{2}{5}$$

Cancellation must involve a numerator and denominator pair, and use the same number to divide each numerator and denominator pair.

 MODELS

$$\frac{1}{5} \div \frac{1}{6} = \frac{1}{5} \times \frac{6}{1} = \frac{6}{5}$$

$$\frac{7}{2} \div \frac{9}{5} = \frac{7}{2} \times \frac{5}{9} = \frac{35}{18}$$

$$\frac{5}{4} \div \frac{6}{10} = \frac{5}{4} \times \frac{10}{6} = \frac{50}{24} = \frac{25}{12}$$

$$\frac{5}{7} \times \frac{3}{6} = \frac{15}{42} = \frac{5}{14}$$

$$\frac{5}{4} \times \frac{6}{4} = \frac{30}{16} = \frac{15}{8}$$

$$\frac{2}{5} \times \frac{4}{8} = \frac{8}{40} = \frac{1}{5}$$

? **CRITICAL THINKING QUESTIONS**

1. What is meant by *reciprocal*?

2. Why is it important to know about reciprocals when dividing fractions?

3. When multiplying two fractions, what should you do if a factor in the numerator of one fraction is equal to the factor in the denominator of the other fraction?

4. When dividing two fractions, what should you do if the denominators are equal?

MODULE 12 DECIMAL ADDITION AND SUBTRACTION

BUILDING UNDERSTANDING

When adding and subtracting decimals, you use the very same processes as natural number addition and subtraction but you must also take into account the alignment and placement of the decimal points.

In general, the process of addition or subtraction is made easier and more accurate when the numbers being added or subtracted are vertically aligned in columns. In other words, the digits in the **1's** column should line up, as should the digits in the **10's** column, the **100's** column, and so on. For decimals, this involves lining up columns of digits on *both sides of the decimal point*. The simplest way to do this for any decimal problem is to put the numbers in a column with the decimal points lined up under each other.

In some cases, you may want to include **trailing zeros** at the end of a number to even the number of columns and keep columns lined up. Zeros can be added to the *right* of the last digit or in any unfilled place value position but may *not* be inserted between digits.

After lining up the decimal places, perform the addition or subtraction just as you would with natural numbers. The final sum or difference should have the decimal point placed *directly below* the line of decimal points that were added or subtracted.

For example, suppose you are to subtract **2.829** from **175.6** Which format presented below makes it easier to perform this calculation, A or B?

(A)	(B)
(2 trailing zeros included)	(No trailing zeros included)
175.600	175.6
− 2.829	− 2.829

THINGS TO REMEMBER

1. When adding and subtracting decimal numbers, it is simplest to put the numbers in a column with the decimal points lined up under each other. It is very important to remember to **properly align the position of the decimal places** for each number being added. Digits to both sides of the decimal point should be aligned correctly so that the **1's** digits are lined up in a column, the **10's** digits are lined up in a column, and so on.

2. Follow the rules for integer addition and subtraction. Recall that:

    $$a + (-b) = a - b \quad \text{and} \quad -a + b = b - a = -(a - b)$$

3. Zeros, called "trailing zeros" may be added (to the right of the last digit) to even the columns when adding or subtracting. However, you cannot insert zeros between digits. Trailing zeros do not change the value of the number. Zeros inserted between digits will change the value.

Calculate the following:

3.67 + 59.7423	37.452 − 84.7	−0.856 − (−98.7)	0.8036 − 0.6466
3.6700	− 84.700	98.700	0.8036
+ 59.7423	+ 37.452	− 0.856	− 0.6466
63.4123	−47.248	97.844	0.157

Note: In the second example, since we are subtracting a larger number from a smaller number, we place the larger number on top, "subtract" the bottom number and then put a negative sign in front of the result. (Think back to the number line in the integer addition module, where you would start at −84.7 and move 37.452 to the right. Do you see how you would end up at −47.248? To convince yourself, try easier numbers such as −8 + 3 = −5.)

 CRITICAL THINKING QUESTIONS

1. How does the process of adding decimals differ from adding natural numbers?

2. What are the similarities between the processes of adding decimal numbers and adding natural numbers?

3. What is meant by *trailing zeros* and when may they be used?

4. Why is it so important that the decimal points line up when adding or subtracting a column of decimal numbers?

5. How can you validate that your answers are correct?

BUILDING UNDERSTANDING

When multiplying and dividing decimals, use the same processes as when multiplying and dividing natural numbers, with the additional requirement of correctly placing the decimal point in the final answer.

Decimal Multiplication

Decimal multiplication is least complicated if you perform the multiplication first (as if there were no decimals) and then after the calculation is done, determine where to insert or place the decimal point. Set up the problem so that the digits to be multiplied are lined up to the right and then follow the rules for natural number multiplication.

To determine the correct place to insert the decimal point once you have performed the calculation, count the total number of decimal places (counting from the right) in the numbers you are multiplying and insert the decimal point in the final answer the same number of places from the right. For example, 5.67 has 2 decimal places and 20.271 has 3 decimal places. Use your powers of estimation as a check to make sure that the answer is reasonable.

> **Remember!**
>
> $$\text{Divisor}\overline{)\text{Dividend}}^{\text{Quotient}}$$

Decimal Division

Decimal division is similar to natural number division but it requires that you correctly set-up and place the decimal point in the final answer. **When dividing a decimal number by a whole number,** simply place the decimal point in the answer directly above the decimal point of the dividend before dividing. For example,

$$0.75 \div 25 = 25\overline{)0.75}^{0.03} \quad \text{and} \quad 0.005 \div 5 = 5\overline{)0.005}^{0.001} \quad \text{and} \quad 40.4 \div 20 = 20\overline{)40.40}^{2.02}$$

One way to look at **dividing a decimal number by a decimal number** is to change the divisor so that it becomes a whole number and then we can proceed as we did above (dividing a decimal number by a whole number). However, if we make any changes to the decimal point in the divisor, we must also make the same changes to the dividend.

To convert the divisor to a whole number, move the decimal point to the right as many place values as needed to position it to the right of the divisor digits. Accordingly, move the decimal point in the dividend the same number of places. Insert the decimal point in the quotient and begin the process of division. For example:

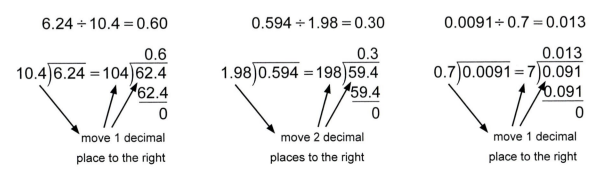

THINGS TO REMEMBER

The commutative property for multiplication states that the order in which numbers are multiplied does not matter; that $a \times b = b \times a$. Therefore, arrange the numbers being multiplied so that there is the least amount of work.

For example, consider, $8.1 \times .4567$

| There is less work involved when the multiplication is set up as: | $\begin{array}{r} 0.4567 \\ \times\ 8.1 \\ \hline \end{array}$ | than in working the problem this way: | $\begin{array}{r} 8.1 \\ \times\ 0.4567 \\ \hline \end{array}$ |

2. Use your skills at estimation as a way to verify that you have put the decimal point in the right location. For example, since 4.3752×0.5278, in round terms, is very close to $4 \times .5 = 2$, you know that in choosing from the following answers, 0.23092, 2.3092, and 23.092, the answer 2.3092 is most reasonable and therefore has the decimal point in the correct place.

3. When dividing a decimal number by a decimal number, be sure to move the decimal point the same number of place values in the dividend as the divisor.

 MODELS

Calculate the following:

| $7.5 \times 9.5 =$ | $0.46 \times 0.022 =$ | $0.0005 \times 7.12 =$ |

$$\begin{array}{rl} 7.5 & \text{1 decimal place} \\ \times\ 9.5 & \text{1 decimal place} \\ \hline 375 & \\ 6750 & \\ \hline 71.25 & \text{2 decimal places} \end{array}$$

$$\begin{array}{rl} 0.46 & \text{2 decimal places} \\ \times\ 0.022 & \text{3 decimal places} \\ \hline 92 & \\ 920 & \\ \hline 0.01012 & \text{5 decimal places} \end{array}$$

$$\begin{array}{rl} 7.12 & \text{2 decimal places} \\ \times\ 0.0005 & \text{4 decimal places} \\ \hline 0.003560 & \text{6 decimal places} \end{array}$$

$$0.85 \div 0.034 = 25.00$$

$$0.034\overline{)0.85} = 34\overline{)\begin{array}{r} 25.0 \\ 850.0 \\ \underline{68} \\ 170 \\ \underline{170} \\ 0 \end{array}}$$

$$4.505 \div 1.7 = 2.65 \qquad 1.7\overline{)4.505} = 17\overline{)\begin{array}{r} 2.65 \\ 45.05 \\ \underline{34} \\ 110 \\ \underline{102} \\ 85 \\ \underline{85} \\ 0 \end{array}}$$

? CRITICAL THINKING QUESTIONS

1. In what way is dividing decimal numbers similar to dividing whole numbers?

2. In what ways does multiplying decimal numbers differ from multiplying whole numbers?

3. How do you determine where to put the decimal point when multiplying two decimal numbers?

4. How do you determine where to put the decimal point when dividing two decimals numbers?

Math and Graphing Skills

BUILDING UNDERSTANDING

Rounding involves shortening the number of digits displayed for a number. It is a common task when working with numbers that contain more digits or decimal places than needed.

In this module, you will be rounding numbers to a certain number of decimal places. Initially, you will be given a number that is displayed to five decimal places and then asked to round this number several times — to four decimal places, three decimal places, two decimal places, one decimal place, and finally to zero decimal places. Rounding to zero decimal places is the same as *"rounding to the nearest integer."* This means using the digits after (to the right of) the decimal place to round the digit just to the left of the decimal place.

Follow the rules of rounding presented below, as you work with rounding decimals.

THINGS TO REMEMBER

Which Digit(s) to Focus on

Decimals are rounded by using the digits that are to the right of the number of decimal places to which you are rounding.

For example, if rounding 4.372

- to one decimal place: look at the right of the number 3, and focus on the number 7 for rounding.

- to two decimal places: look to the right of the number 7, and focus on the number 2 for rounding.

Which Way to Round

Rule	Example
If the digit (to the right of the number of decimal places to which you are rounding) is:	
...greater than 5, round up *increase the digit to be rounded by one*	When rounding 6.37 to one decimal place, increase the digit "3" by one (since the digit "7" is greater than 5), resulting in 6.4
...less than 5. round down *leave the digit to be rounded the same*	when rounding 3.82 to one decimal place, leave the digit " 8 the same (since the digit '2' is less than 5), resulting in 3.8
...is 5 $\Rightarrow$ and there are additional non-zero digits further to the right round up	3.4512 rounded to 1 decimal place rounds up to 3.5
...is 5 $\Rightarrow$ and there are no digits further right, use the "round even rule," that is, if the digit to be rounded is odd then round up, and if the digit to be rounded is even then round down.	3.45 rounded to 1 decimal place uses the round even rule to round down to 3.4 while 3.55 rounded to 1 decimal place uses the round even rule to round up to 3.6

MODELS

Round the following numbers to the designated number of decimal places.

Decimal Places	145.35462	1.29675	23.56445
0	145	1	24
1	145.4	1.3	23.6
2	145.35	1.30	23.56
3	145.355	1.297	23.564
4	145.3546	1.2968	23.5644

? CRITICAL THINKING QUESTIONS

1. When rounding 56.263 to one decimal place, which digit do you use to determine how to round? What is the general rule for deciding which digit to focus on when rounding a number?

2. What is the result of *rounding down*? How is the original number changed?

3. In which circumstances do you "round up" a number?

4. What is the ***round even rule***?

5. How can rounding affect calculations?

Math and Graphing Skills

MODULE 15 CONVERTING COMMON FRACTIONS TO DECIMALS

BUILDING UNDERSTANDING

Numbers of equal value can be represented in different mathematical forms. For example, .75 is the *decimal equivalent* of the fraction $\frac{3}{4}$. At times it is convenient to be able to convert numbers from one form to another.

This module is about changing or converting common fractions to decimals.

> To change a common fraction to an equivalent decimal, divide the numerator by the denominator and write the quotient in decimal form.

$$\text{denominator}\overline{)\text{numerator}}^{\text{decimal}}$$

For example, to convert $\frac{4}{5}$ to a decimal:

$$5\overline{)4.00}^{0.80}$$

THINGS TO REMEMBER

To convert a common fraction to a decimal, divide the numerator by the denominator and write the quotient in decimal form. Follow the rules of division to calculate the decimal equivalent.

When the denominator is less than 10, the table below can be used to change to a decimal using a different method.

$$\frac{1}{2}=0.5 \quad \frac{1}{3}=0.33\overline{3} \quad \frac{1}{4}=0.25 \quad \frac{1}{5}=0.2 \quad \frac{1}{6}=0.16\overline{6} \quad \frac{1}{7}=0.143 \quad \frac{1}{8}=0.125 \quad \frac{1}{9}=0.11\overline{1}$$

Note: when a terminating digit (or group of digits) in a decimal expression repeats, we indicate this by drawing a line over that number or numbers.

$$\text{Since } \frac{3}{8}=3\times\frac{1}{8} \text{ then } \frac{3}{8}=3\times 0.125=0.375$$

$$\text{And } \frac{2}{5}=2\times\frac{1}{5} \text{ then } \frac{2}{5}=2\times 0.2=0.4$$

$$\text{In general, with a fraction } \frac{a}{b}, \qquad \frac{a}{b}=a\times\frac{1}{b}=a\times\left(\text{decimal equivalent of } \frac{1}{b}\right)$$

 **MODELS**

Convert the following fractions to their decimal equivalents:

$$\frac{3}{5} = 5\overline{)3.0}^{\,0.6} \quad \text{or} \quad 3 \times \frac{1}{5} = 3 \times 0.20 = 0.60$$

$$\frac{4}{9} = 9\overline{)4.000}^{\,0.44\overline{4}} \quad \text{or} \quad 4 \times \frac{1}{9} = 4 \times 0.11\overline{1} = 0.44\overline{4}$$

$$\frac{8}{3} = 3\overline{)8.000}^{\,2.66\overline{6}} \quad \text{or} \quad 8 \times \frac{1}{3} = 8 \times 0.33\overline{3} = 2.66\overline{6}$$

? CRITICAL THINKING QUESTIONS

1. List five decimal equivalents of fractions that you know without having to make any calculations.

2. What is the general process for converting a fraction to its decimal equivalent?

3. How can you prove (using calculations) that your answers to Question 1 are correct?

4. When might it be preferable to perform calculations with decimal numbers rather than fractions?

MODULE 16 CONVERTING DECIMALS TO COMMON FRACTIONS

BUILDING UNDERSTANDING

Numbers of equal value can be represented in different mathematical forms. For example, 8/12 is equal to 3/4 which is equal to 0.75. Sometimes it may be necessary to convert numbers from one form to another.

This module is about converting decimals to common fractions. When looking at a decimal, the digits to the right of the decimal point represent a fractional value or value less than one. The process of converting a decimal to a fraction is not difficult if you simply read aloud the decimal correctly. For example:

0.9 is read as "nine tenths" and is written as $\dfrac{9}{10}$

0.28 is read as "twenty eight hundredths" and is written as $\dfrac{28}{100}$

0.145 is read as "one hundred forty-five thousandths" and is written as $\dfrac{145}{1000}$

If there is whole number in front of the decimal, simply write the whole number as is and convert the decimal portion to a fraction:

$$3.75 = 3\dfrac{75}{100} = 3\dfrac{3}{4}$$

THINGS TO REMEMBER

When Converting a Decimal to a Common Fraction:

1. The digits to the **right** of the decimal are converted to the common fraction.

   - The digit(s) to the right of the decimal place become the **numerator** of the common fraction

   - The denominator of the fraction is some power of 10 (10, 100, 1000, . . .) depending on how many digits are to the right of the decimal point; 10 for 1 digit, 100 for 2 digits, 1000 for 3 digits, and so on.

   - Verify that your fraction is correct by reading the decimal aloud

2. Whole numbers to the **left** of the decimal point remain as a whole number followed by the fractional equivalent.

3. ***Remember to reduce the fraction to its lowest terms.*** For example:

Initial Answer		Reduced Answer
$\dfrac{5}{10}$	→	$\dfrac{1}{2}$

Initial Answer		Reduced Answer
$\dfrac{40}{100}$	→	$\dfrac{2}{5}$

MODELS

Convert the following decimals to fractions:

$$0.18 = \frac{18}{100} = \frac{9}{50}$$

$$0.44 = \frac{44}{100} = \frac{11}{25}$$

$$0.315 = \frac{315}{1000} = \frac{63}{200}$$

$$0.484 = \frac{484}{1000} = \frac{121}{250}$$

? CRITICAL THINKING QUESTIONS

1. Which do you find easier, converting from decimals to fractions, or from fractions to decimals? Explain why.

2. When converting from a decimal to a fraction, how do you determine the value of the numerator?

3. When converting from a decimal to a fraction, how do you determine the value of the denominator?

4. How can you validate that you have correctly converted from a decimal to a fraction?

5. When might it be preferable to perform calculations with fractonal numbers rather than decimal numbers?

BUILDING UNDERSTANDING

A *ratio* is a fixed relation in degree or number between two similar things. In mathematical terms, it is the quotient of one quantity divided by another of the same kind, usually expressed as a fraction.

The ratio of x to y is the quotient, $\dfrac{x}{y}$. A ratio may also be viewed as a comparison, as in $\dfrac{3}{4}$ which can be read as "three out of four" or "three compared to four." Note that a ratio must always consist of two numbers.

A *proportion* is an equation that states that two ratios are equal; for example, $\dfrac{a}{b} = \dfrac{c}{d}$. Proportions may be solved by cross multiplication. To do this, simply multiply the numerator of one ratio by the denominator of the other ratio. If $\dfrac{a}{b} = \dfrac{c}{d}$ then $a \times d = b \times c$.

> *Note:* when working with ratios and proportions, it is crucial that there be consistency with units. Within a single ratio, the units associated with the values in the ratio must be the same. In a proportion, the units in the numerator and denominator of both ratios must be the same. The process of unit conversions can be applied so that there is consistency of units (see Module 33: Conversions).

The meaning of the word *percent* comes from two separate words, *per* and *cent*, which means *per one hundred*, or to divide by one hundred. This is expressed by the symbol **%**. To change a percent to a decimal, drop the % symbol and divide the number by 100.

For example, 25% can be expressed as $\dfrac{25}{100} = 0.25$ and 4.5% is the same as $\dfrac{4.5}{100} = 0.045$.

Applications involving percent can be described by the proportion: $\dfrac{a}{b} = \dfrac{P}{100} = \text{Percent}$.

 THINGS TO REMEMBER

The numbers or values in a ratio should always be expressed in the same units.

While it is correct to have a ratio that compares $\dfrac{30\ \text{minutes}}{60\ \text{minutes}}$, it is not correct to have a ratio of $\dfrac{15\ \text{minutes}}{3\ \text{days}}$. However, through the process of unit conversion, 3 days can be converted to an equivalent number of minutes and then used in the ratio:

$$3\ \text{days} \times \frac{24\ \text{hours}}{1\ \text{day}} \times \frac{60\ \text{minutes}}{1\ \text{hour}} = 4320\ \text{minutes}$$

Process	Example
What ratio is a of b? → the ratio A of B can be written as $\dfrac{a}{b}$	**What ratio is 25 of 50?** $$\dfrac{25}{50} = 0.5$$
What is a % of b? → $a\%$ of $b = \dfrac{a}{100} \times b$	**What is 20% of 30?** $$\dfrac{20}{100} \times 30 = \dfrac{600}{100} = 6 \quad \text{or} \quad 0.20 \times 30 = 6$$
a is b % of what number? → $\dfrac{a}{b} = \dfrac{P}{100} = \text{Percent}$	**5 is 10% of what number?** $$\dfrac{5}{b} = \dfrac{10}{100} = 0.10, \quad 5 = (0.10)b$$ $$b = \dfrac{5}{0.10} = 50$$ Or by cross multiplying: $$5 \times 100 = b \times 10$$ $$500 = 10 \times b$$ $$b = 50$$
a is what percent of b? → $\dfrac{a}{b} = \dfrac{P}{100} = \text{Percent}$	**20 is what percent of 80?** $$\dfrac{20}{80} = \text{Percent} = 0.25 \text{ or } 25\%$$

 MODELS

What ratio is 52 of 80?

$$\dfrac{52}{80} = 0.65$$

5 is what percent of 15?

$$\dfrac{5}{15} = 0.33\overline{3} \quad \text{or} \quad 33\%$$

45 is what percent of 15?

$$\dfrac{45}{15} = 3.0 \quad \text{or} \quad 300\%$$

What is 90% of 90?

$$\dfrac{90}{100} \times 90 = \dfrac{8100}{100} = 81 \quad \text{or} \quad 0.90 \times 90 = 81$$

15 is 67% of what number?

$$\dfrac{a}{b} = \dfrac{67}{100} = 0.67, \quad (0.67)b = 15, \quad b = \dfrac{15}{0.67} = 22.388$$

$$\text{or } 15 \times 100 = 67 \times b, \quad b = 22.388$$

1. How do you change a percent to a decimal?

2. What is the difference between a ratio and a proportion?

3. If 30 is 75% of a number, is the number greater than or less than 30? Why?

4. If 10 is 50% (or half) of a number, what is that number (without using a pencil and paper)? How can you use the same thought process to solve similar problems which involve more complex numbers?

5. What are three of the most important points you would share with someone who is just learning about ratios and percents?

6. How can you validate that your answers are correct?

BUILDING UNDERSTANDING

Exponents allow us to write large numbers in a more concise form and express repeated multiplication in a more useful and condensed manner.

Just as it is more convenient to use multiplication rather than having to add the same number over and over again, exponentiation simplifies the process of performing repeated multiplication.

Consider $3 \times 3 \times 3 \times 3 \times 3 = 3^5$. When using the format, 3^5, the number 3 is called the **base**, and the 5 (superscripted) is called the **exponent**.

Let's look at *multiplying* two expressions with the same base. For example:

$$5^4 \times 5^2 = (5 \times 5 \times 5 \times 5) \times (5 \times 5) = 5 \times 5 \times 5 \times 5 \times 5 \times 5 = 5^6 = 5^{(4+2)}$$

in general, $a^n \times a^m = a^{(n+m)}$

Now let's look at *dividing* two expressions with the same base. For example:

$$\frac{8^5}{8^3} = \frac{8 \times 8 \times 8 \times 8 \times 8}{8 \times 8 \times 8} = 8 \times 8 = 8^2$$

in general, $\dfrac{a^n}{a^m} = a^{(n-m)}$

Note that the three 8's in the denominator cancel with three of the 8's in the numerator, leaving two 8's.

What if when dividing two expressions with the same base, the exponent of the denominator is greater than the exponent in the numerator?

$$\frac{4^3}{4^5} = \frac{4 \times 4 \times 4}{4 \times 4 \times 4 \times 4 \times 4} = \frac{1}{4 \times 4} = \frac{1}{4^2} \text{ applying } \frac{a^n}{a^m} = a^{(n-m)}: \frac{4^3}{4^5} = 4^{(3-5)} = 4^{-2}$$

Note that $4^{-2} = \dfrac{1}{4^2}$ from looking at the calculations done above.

in general, $a^{-n} = \dfrac{1}{a^n}$

THINGS TO REMEMBER

Concept	Example	Note
$0^n = 0$	$0^3 = 0$	When n is not equal to zero
$1^n = 1$	$1^8 = 1$	When n is not equal to zero

Concept	Example	Note
$a^1 = a$	$5^1 = 5$	
$a^0 = 1$	$7^0 = 1$	When a is not equal to zero
$a^{-n} = \dfrac{1}{a^n}$	$2^{-3} = \dfrac{1}{2^3} = \dfrac{1}{8}$	When a is not equal to zero
$a^n \times a^m = a^{(n+m)}$	$7^4 \times 7^3 = 7^{(4+3)} = 7^7$	
$\dfrac{a^n}{a^m} = a^{(n-m)}$	$\dfrac{9^3}{9^{-3}} = 9^{(3-(-3))} = 9^6$	When a is not equal to zero
$(a^n)^m = a^{(n \times m)}$	$(3^2)^3 = 3^{(2 \times 3)} = 3^6$	

 MODELS

$$4^2 \times 4^5 = 4^{(2+5)} = 4^7 \qquad 8^{-7} \times 8^0 = 8^{-7} \times 1 = 8^{-7}$$

$$\frac{7^{-6}}{7^{-3}} = 7^{(-6-(-3))} = 7^{-3} \qquad \frac{2^{-1}}{2^{-3}} = 2^{(-1-(-3))} = 2^2$$

? CRITICAL THINKING QUESTIONS

1. What occurs when any number is raised to the first power?

2. What is the result of raising any non-zero number to the zero power?

3. What is the difference between multiplying two expressions which have the same base and dividing two expressions which have the same base?

4. Why does $4^2 \times 4^5 = 4^{(2+5)}$?

5. How can you validate that your answers are correct?

 **BUILDING UNDERSTANDING**

When simplifying and solving arithmetic expressions and equations, it is sometimes unclear which operation to perform first. Without an agreed upon plan or approach, there could be many different answers to the same problem. For example, what is the answer to the following expression $6 + 12 \div 2 \times 3$? Is it **27**, **36**, **3**, **8**, or **24**? All these answers are possible, depending on the order in which you add, multiply, and divide.

When we think of multiplication as repeated addition, we can see that multiplication is more powerful than addition. By the same token, exponentiation, which is repeated multiplication, is more powerful still. So a natural order of operation develops where we perform the most powerful operations first. The ***order of operations*** is a universally agreed upon plan for properly simplifying equations and expressions. The steps for the order of operations are presented below.

METHODOLOGY

Simplify within **parentheses**.

Perform **exponentiation**.

Perform **multiplication** and **division** *as they appear from left to right.*

Perform **addition** and **subtraction** *as they appear from left to right.*

There is a useful phrase to help you remember the order: **P**lease **E**xcuse **M**y **D**ear **A**unt **S**ally.

 THINGS TO REMEMBER

1. Summary of the order of operations.

   Level 1 — Parentheses: Operations within parentheses are performed first. If there are several sets of parentheses, begin with the innermost and continue outward.

   Level 2 — Exponentiation: Assuming there are no parentheses (or operations within parentheses have already been performed), exponentiation is performed before any multiplication, division, addition, or subtraction.

   Level 3 — Multiplication and Division: Assuming there are no parentheses or exponentiation remaining, multiplication and division are calculated before addition and subtraction. When two operations are at the same level, the order of operation is from left to right

   Level 4 — Addition and Subtraction: When parentheses, exponentiation, multiplication and division have been performed, then addition and subtraction takes place. Again, when two operations are at the same level, the order of operation is from left to right.

2. Remember the rules for integer operations.

3. Expressions with fractions are simplified as if the numerator is in parentheses and the denominator is in parentheses.

4. When validating a solution or evaluating a formula for specific values, follow the order of operations.

 MODELS

Evaluate the following expressions:

$24 - 3 \times (4 \div 2 + 3) =$ *focus on parentheses first*

$24 - 3 \times (2 + 3) =$ *divide before adding*

$24 - 3 \times 5 =$ *multiply before subtracting*

$24 - 15 =$

9

$3 - (4 \times 2 - 5)^2 + 4 - 2^3 =$ *focus on parentheses first; multiplication first*

$3 - (8 - 5)^2 + 4 - 2^3 =$ *perform exponentiation*

$3 - 3^2 + 4 - 2^3 =$ *perform operations from left to right*

$3 - 9 + 4 - 8 =$

$-6 + 4 - 8 =$

$-2 - 8 =$

−10

$2 \times 5 \times (-3) \div 6 + 8 \div 4 \times (-5) \div 2 =$ *multiplication and division first, left to right*

$10 \times (-3) \div 6 + 2 \times (-5) \div 2 =$

$-30 \div 6 + (-10) \div 2 =$

$-5 + (-5) =$

−10

? **CRITICAL THINKING QUESTIONS**

1. Why do we need an order of operations?

2. If there are no parentheses, why is exponentiation performed before anything else?

3. Why are multiplication and division performed before addition and subtraction?

BUILDING UNDERSTANDING

When the numbers we work with become very large or very small in magnitude, conventional number notation becomes unwieldy. *Scientific notation* makes it possible to express numbers more compactly by writing a number as the product of two factors: a number between 1 and 10 and integral power of 10 (multiplied by some power of 10). Sometimes the letter "E" is used in scientific notation (not to be confused with the "*e*" associated with natural logarithms). In scientific notation, the number that follows the letter E is the power to which 10 is raised. For example,

$$\text{E } 3 = 10^3 \text{ and E } -2 = 10^{-2}$$

The number of significant digits displayed for a number provides information about the degree of accuracy that is intended. In scientific notation, the digits displayed before multiplying by a power of 10 are an indication of the degree of significance;

2 E3 has one significant digit while 3.4398 E−2 has five significant digits.

Trailing zeros are used in scientific notation to indicate increased accuracy (e.g., 7.8 E3 has two significant digits while 7.800 E3 has four significant digits). To illustrate, suppose you are estimating the mileage between two cities and you know it to be about 200 miles. In this case, you would display the number 200 as 2×10^2 or 2 E2 with one significant digit. However, if you know the mileage to be exactly 200 miles, then you would want to display 200 as 2.00×10^2 or 2.00 E2, with three significant digits.

METHODOLOGY

Changing a Decimal to Scientific Notation

For numbers greater than one:

1. Write only the significant digits of the number with a decimal point after the first digit.

2. Multiply the number from Step 1 by a power of 10. The power is the number of places between the present location of the decimal point and its location in the original number.

For numbers less than one:

1. Write only the significant digits of the number with a decimal point after the first digit.

2. Multiply the number from Step 1 by a negative power of 10. The power is equal to the number of places between the present location of the decimal point and its location in the original number.

Note: to change a number in scientific notation to a decimal, perform the inverse of this process.

THINGS TO REMEMBER

Concept	Explanation	Example
$1\ En = 1 \times 10^n = 10^n$	positive power of 10	$1\ E4 = 1 \times 10^4 = 10{,}000$
$1\ E{-}n = 1 \times 10^{-n} = 10^{-n}$	negative power of 10	$1\ E{-}3 = 1 \times 10^{-3} = 0.001$
$abc.d = a.bcd\ E2$	significant digits	$853.4 = 8.534\ E2$ (4 significant digits)
$0.00abcd = a.bcd\ E{-}3$	accuracy of leading zeros	$0.0000057 = 5.7\ E{-}6$ (2 significant digits)
$0.abc00 = a.bc00\ E{-}2$	accuracy using trailing zeros	$0.24500 = 2.4500\ E{-}1$ (5 significant digits)

MODELS

Write the following numbers in scientific notation:

$$1113.8 \quad = \quad 1.1138\ E3 \quad = \quad 1.1138 \times 10^3$$

$$198590 \quad = \quad 1.98590\ E5 \quad = \quad 1.98590 \times 10^5$$

$$0.00000048 \quad = \quad 4.8\ E{-}7 \quad = \quad 4.8 \times 10^{-7}$$

$$0.000670 \quad = \quad 6.70\ E{-}4 \quad = \quad 6.70 \times 10^{-4}$$

CRITICAL THINKING QUESTIONS

1. What are the benefits of using scientific notation? Name at least two.

2. How do you know that a number is written in scientific notation? Where is the decimal always located?

3. What does the letter E stand for in scientific notation?

4. What does it mean to have a negative power attached to a number?

5. How do you know how many significant digits to display?

MODULE 21 · ESTIMATION

BUILDING UNDERSTANDING

Estimation is the process of approximating a result by rounding numbers to one or two significant digits when making calculations. Estimation simplifies problems and makes them easier to work, especially when a calculator is not available.

Estimation is most useful for doing calculations when you don't have access to a calculator, and when the calculations you perform do not require an exact answer. This module will require you to use your knowledge about the order of operations, scientific notation, and exponents.

METHODOLOGY

1. Round the numbers to the desired number of significant digits (one or two significant digits is generally sufficient).

2. Convert the numbers to scientific notation.

3. As you perform the required calculations, follow the rules for order of operations.

Example	$189 - 87 \times 3^3$
Step 1	$200 - 90 \times 30$
Step 2	2 E2 – 9 E1 × 3 E1
Step 3	2 E2 – 27 E2 = –25 E2 = –2.5 E3

Example	$117 \times 134 - (140 - 42)$
Step 1	$120 \times 150 - 100$
Step 2	1.2 E2 × 1.5 E2 – 1 E2
Step 3	1.8 E4 – 1 E2 = 180 E2 – 1 E2 = 179 E2 = 1.79 E4

THINGS TO REMEMBER

1. When adding or subtracting numbers in scientific notation, the exponents for the powers of 10 must be the same. If the powers are not the same, convert to the same power before adding or subtracting.

   For example, 3.4 E2 + 5.6 E2 = 9.0 E2 is allowed because both numbers were expressed as numbers raised to the second power.

   We cannot subtract 6 E2 – 2.3 E 3 without *first* converting the numbers to the same power.

   We can change the first number so that it is expressed as a power of **3**:

   0.6 E3 – 2.3 E3 = –1.7 E3

   Or we can change the second number so that it is expressed as a power of **2**:

   6 E2 – 23 E2 = –17 E2 = –1.7 E3

Math and Graphing Skills

2. Review the rules for the order of operations from Module 19.

3. Review the rules for exponents from Module 18.

4. Review working with numbers in scientific notation from Module 20.

 MODELS

Determine a value for the following expressions.

Note: Sometimes, it is easier to not use scientific notation — use your judgment!

The symbol $\approx$ is used to indicate an approximation, rather than $=$.

$134 \div 92 - (192 - 146)$
$\approx 130 \div 100 - (200 - 150)$
$\approx 1.3 - 50 \approx 49 \approx \mathbf{-4.9\,E1}$

$20 \div 175 \times (161 + 92)$
$\approx 20 \div 200 \times (150 + 100)$
$\approx 0.1 \times 250 \approx 25 \approx \mathbf{2.5\,E1}$

$184 + 52 \times (115 + 152)$
$\approx 200 + 50 \times (120 + 150)$
$\approx 200 + 50 \times 300$
$\approx 2\,E2 + 5\,E1 \times 3\,E2$
$\approx 2\,E2 + 15\,E3$
$\approx 0.2\,E3 + 15\,E3$
$\approx 15.2\,E3 \approx \mathbf{1.52\,E4}$

$182 \times 122 \times (148 - 189)$
$\approx 200 \times 120 \times (150 - 200)$
$\approx 2\,E2 \times 1.2\,E2 \times (-5\,E1)$
$\approx 2.4\,E4 \times (-5\,E1)$
$\approx 2.4\,E4 \times (-0.005\,E4)$
$\approx -0.012\,E4 \approx \mathbf{-1.2\,E6}$

$$169 \div 152 + (74 \times 50) \approx 200 \div 200 + (100 \times 50)$$
$$\approx 1 + (1\,E2 \times 5\,E1) \approx 1 + 5\,E3 \approx \mathbf{5\,E3}$$

PLEASE NOTE: Because this module is about estimation, the approximations given above are just that — estimated answers. In working these problems, you may very well use different numbers and arrive at answers that differ from those above.

? CRITICAL THINKING QUESTIONS

1. What prior knowledge and skills are most useful when estimating?

2. Why does working in scientific notation make multiplication with larger numbers easier?

3. When working with numbers expressed in scientific notation, what is the difference between multiplying and dividing as compared to adding and subtracting?

4. What is the relationship between estimation and the magnitude of answers to calculations?

BUILDING UNDERSTANDING

An equation such as $y = x^2$ describes a relationship between two variables, x and y. Given a value for x (3 in this case), we can calculate the corresponding value for y: $y = 3^2 = 9$. If we perform these calculations for different values of x, we can make a table of input "x" values and their corresponding output "y" values (see Table 22.1 below).

This process can be thought of as a "function machine" with values of x as input and values of y as output. A *function*, $y = f(x)$, is a relationship relative to the x- and y-axes (plural of "axis"), where each value of x has a unique corresponding y-value.

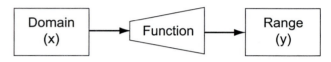

The allowed input values for x are the *domain* of the function. Most of the time, x can be any number, but sometimes it is restricted (for example, $y = 1/x$ is not defined at the value of $x = 0$, so its domain does not include 0). The *range* of a function is the set of all the y-values that result from the function operating on its domain.

A table of x and corresponding y-values may be presented graphically by using a *Cartesian* or *rectangular coordinate system* which consists of x- and y-axes and an *origin* (defined as the point $x = 0$, $y = 0$).

Table 22.1

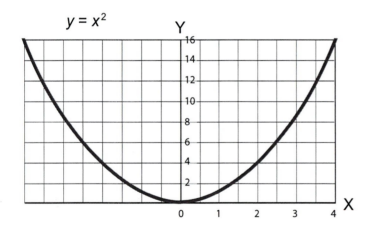

$y = x^2$

x	y
−4	16
−3	9
−2	4
−1	1
0	0
1	1
2	4
3	9
4	16

A number scale is set up along the x-axis with positive numbers extending to the right of the origin and negative numbers extending to the left of the origin. The y-axis is similar with positive numbers extending above the origin and negative numbers extending below the origin. *Note: The number scales on the two axes need not be the same.*

A point may be represented in this coordinate system by starting at the origin and moving a distance along the x-axis, in either the positive or negative direction. This gives the x-coordinate of the point. Then from that location on the x-axis move a distance in either the positive or negative distance direction along the y-axis. This gives the y-coordinate of the point. Combining the x- and y-coordinates yields an ordered pair (x, y), which describes this as a unique point in the coordinate plane.

When Given a *y*-value and Asked to Determine the Corresponding *x*-value:

1. Move up (positive value) or down (negative value) along the y-axis until you reach the given *y*-value.
2. Move along the grid line at the given *y*-value until you reach the function on the graph.
3. From the point on the graph, move along a vertical line until you reach the x-axis to determine the *x*-value.

When Given an *x*-value and Asked to Determine the Corresponding *y*-value:

1. Move right (positive value) or left (negative value) along the x-axis until you reach the given *x*-value.
2. Move along the grid line at the given *x*-value until you reach the function on the graph.
3. From the point on the graph, move along a horizontal line until you reach the *y*-axis to determine the *y*-value.

 THINGS TO REMEMBER

To accurately read values from a graph, be sure to take note of the spacing of the grid lines and the corresponding increments between grids. If for example, the x-axis has 3 grid lines (or tick marks) between 0 and 20, then the increment value between each grid line is 5.

 **MODELS**

Here are examples of the type of problems you will see on the computer:

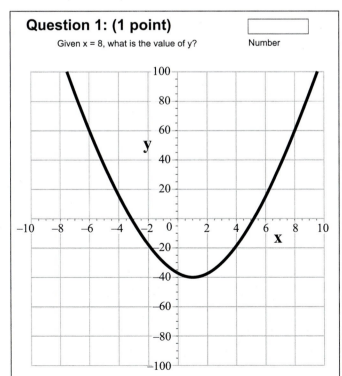

Question 1: (1 point)

Given x = 8, what is the value of y?   Number

To determine the *y*-value when *x* = 8:

Move along the x-axis until you reach 8.

Move up along the grid line until you reach the line on the graph.

Read the value of *y* where the graph crosses the *x*-value of 8.

The *y*-value appears to lie at *y* = 60.

Question 2: (1 point)

Given y = –40, what is the value of x?

Number [ ]

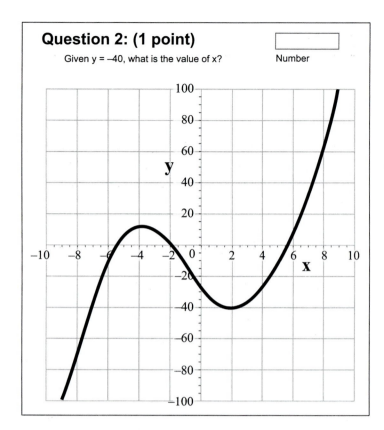

Determine the *x*-value when *y* = –40

Move along the *y*-axis until you reach –40.

Move along that grid line until you reach the point where the graph intersects that gridline. Note that the *y*-axis tick marks are in increments of 5 units.

Be careful! There may be MORE THAN ONE place where the graph crosses this grid line.

Move up or down a vertical line from that point to determine the *x*-value or values. Note that the *x*-axis tick marks are in increments of 0.5 units.

The *x*-values are: $x = -7$ and $x = 2$

? CRITICAL THINKING QUESTIONS

1. What is meant by *Cartesian coordinate system*?

2. How do you determine the location of an ordered pair (*x*, *y*) on a graph?

3. What is the relationship between a function and the corresponding ordered pair values in a table?

4. How do you determine the value for the spacing between grid lines?

5. Given a specific *x*-value, how do you find the corresponding *y*-value on a graph?

▦ BUILDING UNDERSTANDING

The slope of a line is a way to measure its steepness and gain information about the direction and rate of change. The **slope** is the ratio of vertical change (the rise) to horizontal change (the run) when moving from one point on a line to another. The slope of a line can be calculated if any two points on the line are known using the slope formula:

$$\text{Slope} = \frac{\text{rise}}{\text{run}} = m = \frac{y_2 - y_1}{x_2 - x_1} \quad \text{where } (x_1, y_1) \text{ and } (x_2, y_2) \text{ are points on the line}$$

The point where the line crosses the x-axis (where $y = 0$) is called the **x-intercept**.

The point where the line crosses the y-axis (where $x = 0$) is called the **y-intercept**.

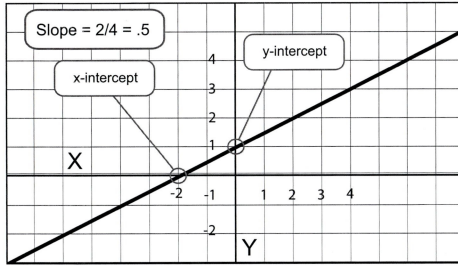

The slope may be calculated using **any two points** on the line.

For ease of calculation, we will use the x- and y-intercepts: $(-2, 0)$ and $(0, 1)$

The slope is equal to:

$$\frac{0-1}{-2-0} = \frac{-1}{-2} = \frac{1}{2}$$

Let's calculate the slope with two different points on the same line: $(4, 3)$ and $(2, 2)$.

In performing this calculation, we determine that the slope of the line is constant: $\dfrac{3-2}{4-2} = \dfrac{1}{2}$.

A linear equation in two variables can be expressed in more than one way. The following forms of a line are helpful in determining useful information about a line such as its slope, y-intercept, and its equation.

The slope-intercept form of a line is **y = mx + b**, where "**m**" is the slope and "**b**" is the y-value of the y-intercept (the value of y when $x = 0$; this is the value of y where the line crosses the y-axis). For example, the line **y = 2x − 1** is in slope-intercept form; we can see that the slope is 2 (the coefficient of x) and the y-intercept is the point $(0, -1)$.

If we know the slope of a given line and one point on the line, we can easily find the equation of the line by using the point-slope formula for a line.

The point-slope formula for a line is: **$(y - y_1) = m(x - x_1)$** where **m** is the slope and **(x, y)** is a point on the line.

THINGS TO REMEMBER

- Lines sloping up from left to right (rising lines) have positive slopes.
- Lines sloping down from left to right (falling lines) have negative slopes.
- Horizontal lines have a slope of zero. You can determine this by applying the slope formula.
- Vertical lines have undefined slopes. You can determine this by applying the slope formula.
- Parallel lines have the same slope.
- Perpendicular lines have slopes that are negative reciprocals of one another; m and $-\dfrac{1}{m}$.

MODELS

Question 1: (1 point)

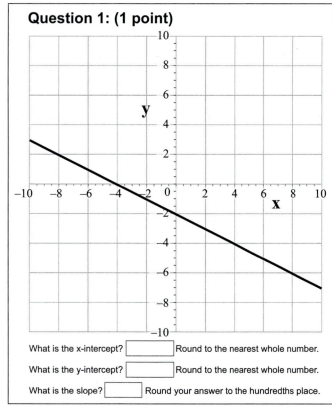

What is the x-intercept? [ ] Round to the nearest whole number.

What is the y-intercept? [ ] Round to the nearest whole number.

What is the slope? [ ] Round your answer to the hundredths place.

At left is an example of the type of problem you will see on the computer.

Choose *any two points on the line* to calculate the slope. We will use the *x*- and *y*-intercepts:

$$x\text{-intercept: } (-4, 0)$$

and

$$y\text{-intercept: } (0, -2)$$

The slope is equal to:

$$\frac{0-(-2)}{-4-0} = \frac{2}{-4} = -\frac{1}{2}$$

 CRITICAL THINKING QUESTIONS

1. What do the terms **x-intercept** and **y-intercept** mean?

2. What is meant by the **slope** of a line and what does it tell you about the direction of the line?

3. How can you determine the **y**-intercept from a linear equation? From a graph?

DISTANCE BETWEEN TWO GRAPHS

BUILDING UNDERSTANDING

In this module, two graphs appear on the screen. At a specified *x*-value, you are to determine the distance between the corresponding *y*-values of the two graphs. In some cases, the *y*-value is given and you must determine the distance between corresponding *x*-values.

This module requires you to be able to read graphs (see Module 23) and then perform subtraction based upon the information contained in a graph.

METHODOLOGY

To Determine the x or y-Distance Between Two Functions on a Graph:

1. Move along the *x*-axis or *y*-axis until you reach the specified *x*-value or *y*-value.

2. Move along the grid line at the given *x*-value or *y*-value until you reach the first graph and determine the corresponding *y*-value or *x*-value

3. Repeat the process to determine the corresponding value for the second graph.

4. The distance between the two *y*-values or *x*-values may be calculated by subtracting one *y*-value or *x*-value from the second value. Be sure to take the absolute value of the difference because distances are always positive!

MODELS

Consider the two graphs at right.

What is the distance between the *x*-values at *y* = –40?

At *y* = –40, the dotted graph has an *x*-value of –2

(–2, –40)

At *y* = –40, the solid graph has an *x*-value of –8

(–8, –40)

The distance between the *x*-values at *y* = –40 is:

–8 – (–2) = |–6| = **6 units**

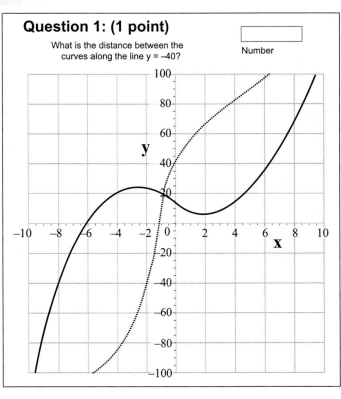

Question 1: (1 point)

What is the distance between the curves along the line *y* = –40?

Number

Consider the two graphs at right.

What is the distance between the *y*-values at *x* = 6?

> At *x* = 6, the dotted graph has a *y*-value of –60 (0, –60).
>
> At *x* = 6, the solid graph has a *y*-value of –20 (6, –20).
>
> The distance between the *y*-values at *x* = 6 is: –60 – 20 = |–40| = **40 units**

What is the distance between the *x*-values at *y* = 20?

> At *y* = 20, the dotted graph has an *x*-value of 5 (5, 20).
>
> At *y* = 20, the solid graph has an *x*-value = –4 (–4, 20).
>
> The distance between the *y*-values at *y* = 20 is: 5 – (–4) = **9 units**

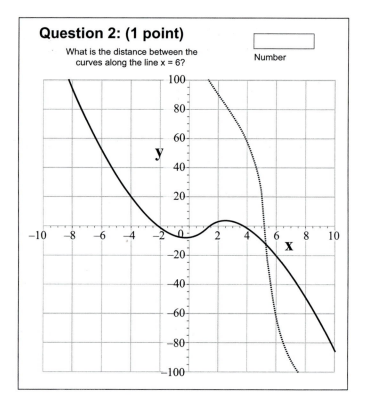

Question 2: (1 point)

What is the distance between the curves along the line x = 6?

[ ] Number

![?] **CRITICAL THINKING QUESTIONS**

1. How do you determine the value on graph if the point lies between two grid lines?

2. Why is it important to take the absolute value of the difference between the *x*- or *y*-values?

3. Can you validate your answer without making any calculations? Explain your answer.

MODULE 25 | POLYNOMIAL ADDITION AND SUBTRACTION

 **BUILDING UNDERSTANDING**

An algebraic expression is made up of terms separated from one another by plus or minus signs. For example, the expression, $4x^2y + xy - 3y + 6$ is made up of four terms: $4x^2y$, xy, $3y$, and 6.

A **monomial** is one term, consisting of a variable, a number, or the product of several of these.

Examples of monomials include: $5a2b$, $-2xy$, $-3z^3$, 4

A **polynomial** is the sum of two or more monomials.
Examples of polynomials include: $9x^3 - 4x + 6$ and $x^2y^2 - 2xy^2 + 3x + 4y + 2$

A **binomial** is a polynomial consisting of two terms while a **trinomial** is a polynomial consisting of three terms. The **coefficient** is the numerical factor of a term.

Adding and Subtracting Polynomials

1. *To add polynomials*: add the coefficients of like terms in the polynomials. Sometimes it may be helpful to arrange like terms in vertical columns and add each column separately. Otherwise, consider grouping all the like terms together.

2. *To subtract one polynomial from another*: subtract the coefficients of like terms in the polynomials. Sometimes it may be helpful to arrange like terms in vertical columns and subtract each column separately. Otherwise, consider grouping all the like terms together.

THINGS TO REMEMBER

1. Be sure that you have not omitted any terms in your final answer.

2. If a term does not have a numerical coefficient, then it has an understood 1 as the numerical coefficient.

3. Only add/subtract the coefficients of like terms. Be sure not to mix terms. For example, since $4y^3 + 2y^2$ are not like terms, $4y^3 + 2y^2 = 4y^3 + 2y^2$ **not** $6y^5$.

4. When adding or subtracting similar terms, add or subtract only the coefficients. Do not change the variable itself. For example, $3x^2 + 5x^2 = 8x^2$ **not** $8x^4$.

5. If the problem is not initially arranged in vertical columns, consider rearranging the polynomial so that each type of term has its own column. If you do not use columns, be sure to group all similar terms together.

Add or subtract the following polynomials:

$(3x - 6) - (2x^2 + 4x - 7) = -2x^2 - x + 1$

	$3x$	-6
$-2x^2$	$-4x$	$+7$
$-2x^2$	$-x$	$+1$

$(x^3 - 4x^2 + 7x - 8) + (8x^2 + x + 8) = x^3 + 4x^2 + 8x$

x^3	$-4x^2$	$+7x$	-8
	$+8x^2$	$+x$	$+8$
x^3	$+4x^2$	$+8x$	$+0$

$(-7x^3 - 9x^2 + 7x - 8) - (-x^2 - 3x + 3) = -7x^3 - 8x^2 + 10x - 11$

$-7x^3$	$-9x^2$	$+7x$	-8
	$+x^2$	$+3x$	-3
$-7x^3$	$-8x^2$	$+10x$	-11

$(6x - 5) - (-4x^2 + x + 4) = 4x^2 + 5x - 9$

	$6x$	-5
$4x^2$	$-x$	-4
$4x^2$	$5x$	-9

? CRITICAL THINKING QUESTIONS

1. What is the difference between a monomial and polynomial?

2. What does it mean to *combine like terms*?

3. Why is helpful to add polynomials in vertical columns?

4. What is one possible error to avoid when adding.or subtracting polynomials?

5. How can you validate that your answer is correct?

MODULE 26 POLYNOMIAL MULTIPLICATION

BUILDING UNDERSTANDING

Recall from the previous module that a polynomial expression is made of terms separated from one another by plus or minus signs. A monomial is one term, consisting of a variable, a number, or the product of several of these. A polynomial is the sum of two or more monomials. A binomial is a polynomial with exactly two terms; it is the sum of exactly two monomials.

Multiplication of a Monomial by a Monomial

To multiply one monomial by another monomial, multiply the numerical coefficients and write their literal factors after the product.

$$\left(x^a\right)\left(x^b\right)= x^{(a+b)}$$

For example, $(4x)(2y) = 8xy$ and $(5a)(-4b^2) = -20ab^2$

For example: $(3x^2)(-4x^2y) = -12x^2y$ and $(-3x^2)(-xy^2) = 3x^3y^2$

Multiplication of a Polynomial by a Polynomial

Multiplication of two polynomials is accomplished by multiplying each term of the first polynomial by each term of the second polynomial and then adding the products. Polynomial multiplication makes use of the distributive property which states: $a \times (b + c) = ab + ac$.

METHODOLOGY

Multiplication of a Binomial by a Binomial: $(a + b) \times (c + d)$

Step 1	The product of the *first* terms $(a \times c)$ of each binomial is the *first* term of the final product.
Step 2	The product of the *last* terms $(b \times d)$ of each binomial is the *last* term of final product.
Step 3	The *middle* term of the final product is the sum of the cross products: $(a \times d) + (b \times c)$
Step 4	The final product of the multiplication of a binomial by a binomial is the combination of the products from the first three steps; the first term plus the middle term plus the final term: $(a \times c) + (a \times d) + (b \times c) + (b \times d)$

For example, to find the product of $(3x - 5)(2x + 1)$:

Step 1	first term	$(3x)(2x) = 6x^2$
Step 2	last term	$(-5)(1) = -5$
Step 3	middle term	$(3x)(1) + (-5)(2x) = 3x - 10x = -7x$
Step 4	solution	$6x^2 - 7x - 5$

THINGS TO REMEMBER

1. The Distributive Property is used when multiplying polynomials. The distributive property states: $a \times (b + c) = ab + ac$. For example:

$$3(2x + 5) = 3(2x) + 3(5) = 6x + 15$$

2. Reversing the distributive property is called **factoring** and $a \times (b + c)$ is the *factored form* of $ab + ac$.

3. Multiplication of two polynomials is accomplished by multiplying each term of one polynomial by each term of the other polynomial and then adding the products.

 ## MODELS

Multiply the following polynomials:

$(-4x - 8)(5x - 4) = -20x^2 + 16x - 40x + 32 = -20x^2 - 24x + 32$

$2x^2 (5x^3 - 2x^2 + x - 7) = 10x^5 - 4x^4 + 2x^3 - 14x^2$

$(4x - 3)(-5x^2 + 4x + 5) = $

$$
\begin{aligned}
&-20x^3 + 16x^2 + 20x &&\text{product of } (4x)(-5x^2 + 4x + 5)\\
&\quad\ + 15x^2 - 12x - 15 &&\text{product of } (-3)(-5x^2 + 4x + 5)\\
&-20x^3 + 31x^2 + 8x\ - 15 &&\text{solution, final product}
\end{aligned}
$$

$(6x^2 - 3x - 2)(-8x^2 - 5x + 3) = $

$$
\begin{aligned}
&-48x^4 - 30x^3 + 18x^2 &&\text{product of } (6x^2)(-8x^2-5x+3)\\
&\quad +24x^3 + 15x^2\ - 9x &&\text{product of } (-3x)(-8x^2-5x+3)\\
&\qquad\qquad 16x^2 + 10x - 6 &&\text{product of } (-2)(-8x^2-5x+3)\\
&-48x^4 - 6x^3 + 49x^2 + x\ - 6 &&\text{solution, final product}
\end{aligned}
$$

? CRITICAL THINKING QUESTIONS

1. Why does $(x^3)(x^2) = x^5$ but $(x^3) + (x^2)$ does not equal x^5 ?

2. How does the distributive property help in understanding how to multiply polynomials?

3. If you multiply a binomial by a binomial, how many terms will result, **before** you combine any like terms? Why?

4. What is the single most important piece of advice you would give someone who is just learning to multiply polynomials?

BUILDING UNDERSTANDING

When working with models, symbols are often used to represent some quantity or value.

Consider a model for the purchase of three items at a store. The total cost of your purchases is equal to the sum of the price of the first item plus the price of the second item plus the price of the third item *plus* the product of the sales tax and the sum of the price of all three items. Rather than having to write all these words to express this situation, we can simplify things by using symbols (variables) to create a mathematical expression.

Model to determine the total cost of three items purchased at a store:

$$c = p1 + p2 + p3 + (p1 + p2 + p3) \times t$$

c = total cost

$p1$ = price of item 1

$p2$ = price of item 2

$p3$ = price of item 3

t = sales tax % (converted to a decimal equivalent)

When specific values for variables (such as c, $p1$, $p2$, etc.) are known, they may be ***substituted*** into the model. After specific values are substituted into a model, the model may be ***evaluated*** to determine a final value or answer.

For example, if $p1$ = \$8.95, $p2$ = \$25.69, $p3$ = \$15.25, and t = 7.5%

these values are substituted into the model:

$$c = \$8.95 + \$25.69 + \$15.25 + (\$8.95 + \$25.69 + \$15.25) \times .075$$

and the model may now be evaluated to determine the total cost, c:

$$c = \$49.89 + (\$49.89 \times .075) = \$49.89 + \$3.74 = \mathbf{\$53.63}$$

THINGS TO REMEMBER

1. Check to be sure that you have substituted the correct value for each variable in the model or expression.

2. Apply what you have learned from previous modules when evaluating the model. Pay special attention to the order of operations.

 **MODELS**

Evaluate the models below for the following values, $a = -2$, $b = 6$, $c = 4$, $d = -12$

$$\frac{(b-a)}{(c-d)} = \frac{6-(-2)}{4-(-12)} = \frac{8}{16} = \frac{1}{2}$$

$$a \times b \times (c+d) = -2 \times 6 \times (4+(-12)) = -12 \times -8 = 96$$

$$\frac{(d-a)}{(b+c)} = \frac{-12-(-2)}{6+4} = \frac{-10}{10} = -1$$

? CRITICAL THINKING QUESTIONS

1. What is meant by **substitution**?

2. How are models evaluated?

3. How can you validate that you've correctly subsituted values into a model?

4. Using the basic model presented in Building Understanding, consider a revised model for the cost of purchasing the same three items, with a 50% discount on the first item. Does this new model affect what values you substitute into the model? Why or why not?

BUILDING UNDERSTANDING

A *linear equation* is a first-degree equation. This means that none of the variables in a linear equation are raised to a power greater than one.

For example, $3x + 4(x + 1) = 18$ and $\frac{2}{3}x + y = 2$ are linear equations.

$x^2 + 3y = 10$ is *not* a linear equation because the variable x is raised to the second power.

It is important to note that a linear equation is represented graphically by a straight line.

METHODOLOGY

Solving Linear Equations:

Step 1	Clear parentheses and combine like terms.
Step 2	Clear fractions by multiplying **ALL** terms by the common denominator.
Step 3	Add or subtract to get the chosen variable terms on one side of the equal sign and the other terms on the other side.
Step 4	Multiply or divide both sides of the equation by the coefficient of the chosen variable.
Step 5	Validate your solution.

For example, solve the following equation for x: $5x - 2(x + 1) = x + 4$:

Step 1   *Clear parentheses and combine like terms.*

$5x - 2x - 2 = x + 4$
$3x - 2 = x + 4$

Step 2   *Clear fractions by multiplying ALL terms by the common denominator.*

No fractions; skip this step.

Step 3   *Isolate the variable and combine like terms.*

Add 2 to each side: $3x = x + 6$

Subtract x from each side: $2x = 6$

Step 4   *Multiply or divide both sides of the equation by the coefficient of the chosen variable*

Divide each side by 2: $x = 3$

Step 5   *Validate your solution.*

$5(3) - 2(3 + 1) = 3 + 4$
$15 - 8 = 7$
$7 = 7$

Linear Equations in Two Variables

The solution to a linear equation with two variables includes all the points along a particular line. This line can be most easily graphed when the linear equation is written in the form "$y = mx + b$" (see Module 23, Slopes and Intercepts). If one of the variables in the equation is assigned a specific value, the value for the other variable may easily be determined.

For example, in the equation, $y = 2x - 4$

    if we let $x = 2$, then $y = 0$

    and if we let $x = 4$, then $y = 4$

    and at $x = 0$, then $y = 4$

     The figure at right is a graphical representation of this equation

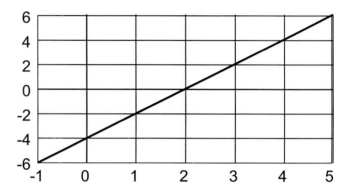

THINGS TO REMEMBER

1. The goal in solving linear equations is to isolate the variable on one side of the equal sign.

2. Simplify by combining like terms whenever possible. Doing so reduces the number of symbols you are working with so that there are fewer opportunities for making a copying error.

3. Whatever you do to one side of the equation (such as adding, subtracting, multiplying, or dividing by a value) be sure to do the same thing to the other side. This keeps the equation "balanced."

4. When you have followed the correct rules of algebra, and have not made a calculation error, the simplified equation is *equivalent* to the original equation. This means that you have rewritten the equation in a simpler form.

MODELS

Solve the following linear equations for the unknown variable:

$-3x + 1 = -1 + 2(-2x + 1)$ $4y + 1 + 2(-3y - 5) = -7$ $5(-5n + 1) - n + 4 = 113$

$-3x + 1 = -1 - 4x + 2$ $4y + 1 - 6y - 10 = -7$ $-25n + 5 - n + 4 = 113$

$-3x + 4x = -1 - 1 + 2$ $4y - 6y = -1 + 10 - 7$ $-25n - n = -5 - 4 + 113$

$x = 0$ $-2y = 2$ $-26n = 104$

                                     $y = -1$ $n = -4$

Note: Be sure to validate your answers!

1. What is meant by the term *linear equation*?

2. Why is it important to combine like terms whenever possible?

3. What will happen if you subtract 10 from only one side of an equation?

4. How do you validate that your solution is correct?

5. What is the connection between solving an equation and evaluating an expression? What is the same? What is different? Explain your answers.

BUILDING UNDERSTANDING

In a mathematical equation, the equal sign (=) is used to signify that what is to the left of the equal sign is *equivalent* to what is to the right of the equal sign. In some cases however, the two quantities may not be equal (for instance, one quantity may be larger or smaller than the other). These types of equations are called ***inequalities***. There are specific symbols used to express different kinds of inequalities. They are as follows:

≠ not equal	$a \neq b$	(a is not equal to b)
> greater than	$a > b$	(a is greater than b)
≥ or >= greater than or equal to	$a \geq b$	(a is greater than or equal to b)
< less than	$a < b$	(a is less than b)
≤ or <= less than or equal to	$a \leq b$	(a is less than or equal to b)

Solving Linear Inequalities

Linear inequalities are solved in a manner very similar to that used when solving linear equations (as described in the previous module) **with one important exception:** When multiplying or dividing by a negative number, the direction of the inequality sign ***must*** be reversed.

To understand why the inequality sign is reversed when multiplying or dividing by a negative number, consider a number line and the locations of the numbers, 2 and 8, and −2 and −8.

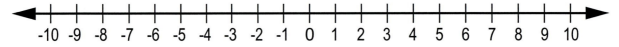

-10 -9 -8 -7 -6 -5 -4 -3 -2 -1 0 1 2 3 4 5 6 7 8 9 10

On the positive side of the number line, two is less than eight (2 < 8) is a true statement. However, on the negative side of the number line, when each side in multiplied by −1, then the statement, minus two is less than minus eight (−2 < −8) is NOT true. Changing the direction of the inequality symbol makes the statement true: −2 > −8.

THINGS TO REMEMBER

1. The inequality $x > a$ can also be written as $a < x$. For example, $x > 5$ is the same as $5 < x$. *Note:* the wide end of the greater than and less than symbol *opens towards* the larger quantity while the narrow end *points to* the smaller quantity.

2. You can add and subtract the same number from both sides of an inequality. For example, if $x - 3 > 5$, then adding to 3 to each side of the inequality gives $x > 8$.

3. You can multiply or divide both sides of an inequality by the same *positive* number. For example, if $\frac{x}{2} > 5$, then multiplying each side of the inequality by 2 gives $x > 10$.

4. When you multiply or divide both sides of an inequality by a negative number, you must reverse the direction of the inequality symbol for the statement to remain true.

MODELS

Solve the following inequalities:

$2y - 1 - 2(-5y + 4) \leq -69$ $6(-3x - 2) + 2x + 3 > -57$ $2z - (3z + 5) < 4z + 10$

$2y - 1 + 10y - 8 \leq -69$ $-18x - 12 + 2x + 3 > -57$ $2z - 3z - 5 < 4z + 10$

$12y - 9 \leq -69$ $-16x - 9 > -57$ $-1z - 4z < 5 + 10$

$12y \leq -60$ $-16x > -48$ $-5z < 15$

$y \leq -5$ $x < 3$ $z > -3$

Note: Be sure to validate your answers!

? CRITICAL THINKING QUESTIONS

1. What is a linear inequality?

2. What is the difference in meaning between the symbols > and ≥ ?

3. In what way(s) is working with linear inequalities similar to working with linear equations?

4. Why must you reverse the direction of the inequality sign if you multiply or divide by a negative number?

5. How do you validate that your solution is correct?

MODULE 30 | QUADRATIC EQUATIONS

BUILDING UNDERSTANDING

Recall that first-degree or linear equations have variables raised to the first power and no higher. Linear equations are always represented graphically as straight lines. *Quadratic equations,* also called *second-degree polynomial equations*, are represented graphically as parabolas.

The standard form for quadratic equations is:

$$ax^2 + bx + c = 0 \quad \text{(where a, b, and c are constants, and } a \neq 0\text{)}$$

Solving a Quadratic Equation by Factoring

Sometimes the quickest way to solve a quadratic equation is by factoring, a process which draws on your knowledge of factoring polynomials and solving linear equations (a quadratic equation is the product of two binomials). *Please note* that no module in *Math and Graphing Skills* covers factoring polynomials (in this case, trinomials), so you will need to have learned that skill from another source before you can work on this module.

An algebraic procedure for solving the standard form of quadratic equations is based on a certain principle (the zero factor property) involving the product of two numbers. In general, if $a \times b = 0$ (a situation where the product of two factors is equal to zero), then one or both of the factors must be equal to zero *(if $a \times b = 0$, then $a = 0$ and/or $b = 0$)*.

This principle makes it possible to solve a quadratic equation if it can be changed into the form of two factors whose product is equal to zero. Each factor may then be set equal to zero and the value of the variable determined, for each factor. The solutions to quadratic equations are called **roots**.

METHODOLOGY

Solving Quadratic Equations by Factoring:

Step 1	Determine that the equation is quadratic.
Step 2	Rewrite the equation in standard form.
Step 3	Factor the polynomial (into two binomial factors).
Step 4	Set each factor equal to zero and solve each factor for the variable. Solve for the roots.
Step 5	Validate your solution by substituting each of the roots individually into the original equation.

Solve: $x^2 + 8x + 15 = 0$

Step 1   *The equation is quadratic.*

Step 2   *The equation is already written in standard form.*

Step 3 $(x + 3)(x + 5) = 0$

Step 4 $x + 3 = 0, x = -3$ $\qquad\qquad$ $x + 5 = 0, x = -5$ $\qquad\qquad$ The roots are -3 and -5.

Step 5 $(-3)^2 + 8(-3) + 15 = 0$ $\qquad$ $(-5)^2 + 8(-5) + 15 = 0$

$\qquad\qquad$ $9 - 24 + 15 = 0$ $\qquad\qquad\qquad$ $25 - 40 + 15 = 0$

$\qquad\qquad$ $0 = 0$ ✓ $\qquad\qquad\qquad\qquad$ $0 = 0$ ✓

THINGS TO REMEMBER

It is important that you validate your solutions. Do this by substituting each of the roots individually into the original equation and verifying that the result is a true statement.

MODELS

Solve the following quadratic equations:

$2t^2 + 11t + 5 = 0$	$-18y^2 + 2 = 0$	$10x^2 - 32x + 6 = 0$
$(2t + 1)(t + 5) = 0$	$(-3y + 1)(6y + 2) = 0$	$(10x - 2)(x - 3) = 0$
$2t + 1 = 0 \qquad t + 5 = 0$	$-3y + 1 = 0 \quad 6y + 2 = 0$	$10x - 2 = 0 \quad x - 3 = 0$
$2t = -1$	$-3y = -1 \qquad 6y = -2$	$10x = 2$
$t = -\dfrac{1}{2} \qquad t = -5$	$y = \dfrac{1}{3} \qquad y = -\dfrac{1}{3}$	$x = \dfrac{1}{5} \qquad x = 3$

Validate:	Validate:	Validate:
$2(-1/2)^2 + 11(-1/2) + 5 = 0$	$(-18)(1/3)^2 + 2 = 0$	$10(1/5)^2 - 32(1/5) + 6 = 0$
$1/2 - 11/2 + 5 = 0$ ✓	$(-18)(1/9) + 2 = 0$	$2/5 - 32/5 + 30/5 = 0$ ✓
	$-2 + 2 = 0$ ✓	
$2(-5)^2 + 11(-5) + 5 = 0$	$(-18)(-1/3)^2 + 2 = 0$	$10(3)^2 - 32(3) + 6 = 0$
$50 - 55 + 5 = 0$ ✓	$-2 + 2 = 0$ ✓	$90 - 96 + 6 = 0$ ✓

? CRITICAL THINKING QUESTIONS

1. How can you tell that an equation is quadratic?

2. What is meant by ***a quadratic equation in standard form***?

3. How can you validate that the roots you calculated are correct?

MODULE 31 SIMULTANEOUS EQUATIONS

BUILDING UNDERSTANDING

A set of equations that contains the same variables is called a ***system of equations*** or ***simultaneous equations***. Solving a system of equations requires that you find the values for the variables that satisfy all the equations in the set.

In this module, we look at solving two first-degree equations. Recall that these equations have no variables at a power greater than one (no variables such as x^2 or higher) and when graphed, linear equations are straight lines. Two straight lines (unless parallel or the same line) will always intersect at one point (ordered pair of numbers). This point of intersection represents the one common solution to the two simultaneous first-degree equations.

METHODOLOGY

Simultaneous equations may be solved either graphically or algebraically.

Graphical Solution

A system of two equations can be presented graphically to find the solution that occurs at the point where the two lines intersect. Unless parallel (or the same line), two linear equations graphed on the same axes will intersect at a point. One line represents the ordered pairs that satisfy the first equation and the other line represents the ordered pairs that satisfy the second equation. The ordered pair where both lines intersect satisfies both equations and is the simultaneous solution of the pair of equations.

Algebraic Solutions

Algebraically there are two common methods for solving simultaneous first-degree equations. One method involves **elimination** of one variable by addition or subtraction and the second by the method of **substitution**.

Elimination Method

The elimination method is most useful when you are able to make the coefficients of one of the variables into an additive inverses of the other — when added together, they are canceled or eliminated. Examples of added inverses are: $2x$ and $-2x$, $4y$ and $-4y$, z and $-z$. With one variable eliminated, you can easily solve for the other variable. Once you know one value, you can solve for the value of the second variable.

Step 1	Put both equations in the form: $ax + by = c$
Step 2	Modify the equations if necessary in order to eliminate one variable by addition of additive inverses. If necessary, multiply both sides of one or both equations to produce coefficients of one variable that are additive inverses.
Step 3	Eliminate the variable by adding or subtracting the two equations.

Step 4	Solve the resulting one-variable equation for that variable.
Step 5	Substitute the value of the first variable in either of the two original equations to solve for the value of the second variable.
Step 6	Validate your solution.

Step 1 $2x - 6y = 0$
$x - 6y = -3$

Step 2 The additive inverse of 2 is –2. Multiply each side of the second equation by –2 to eliminate the variable x.

$-2(x - 6y) = -2(-3)$
$-2x + 12y = 6$

Step 3 $2x - 6y = 0$
$\underline{-2x + 12y = 6}$
$6y = 6$

Step 4 $y = 1$

Step 5 $2x - 6(1) = 0$
$2x = 6$
$x = 3$

The solution is $x = 3$, $y = 1$ which is the point (3, 1).

Step 6 $2(3) - 6(1) = 0$
$6 - 6 = 0$ ✓

$3 - 6(1) = -3$
$3 - 6 = -3$ ✓

Substitution Method

A first-degree equation can always be solved if it contains only one variable. In an equation with two variables, one way of eliminating a variable is to substitute or replace a variable by an expression to which it is equal. You must first solve either equation for one variable in terms of the other variable. The resulting expression can be substituted for the variable in the second equation, producing an equation with only one variable. Once one value is known, the second can be solved for by substitution.

Step 1	Solve either equation for one variable in terms of the other.
Step 2	Substitute the resulting expression for the first variable which eliminates that variable.
Step 3	Solve the resulting one variable equation for that variable.
Step 4	Substitute the value of the first variable in either of the two original equations to solve for the value of the second variable.
Step 5	Validate your solution.

Equations: $2x - 6y = 0$ and $x - 6y = -3$

Step 1 $x = 6y - 3$

Step 2 $2(6y - 3) - 6y = 0$

Step 3 $12y - 6 - 6y = 0$
$6y = 6$, $y = 1$

Step 4 $2x - 6(1) = 0$
$2x = 6$, $x = 3$

The solution is $x = 3$, $y = 1$ which is the point (3, 1)

Step 5 $2(3) - 6(1) = 0$ $3 - 6(1) = -3$
$6 - 6 = 0$ ✓ $3 - 6 = -3$ ✓

THINGS TO REMEMBER

1. Use the elimination method when it is easy to manipulate the coefficients of a variable to get create an additive inverse. Otherwise, use the method of substitution.

2. Always make sure that you have solved for the values for both variables. The answer should be presented as an ordered pair (*x, y*), or as *x* = value, and *y* = value.

3. Validate your answers by substituting the values back into both equations.

MODELS

Solve the following simultaneous equations.

$2x + 3y = -13$ and $2x + 6y = -16$	$-4x - 4y = -20$ and $6x - 3y = 12$
Use Elimination Method:	Use Substitution Method:
Multiply each side of second equation by –1. $-2x - 6y = 16$	Divide each side of first equation by –4. $x = -y + 5$
Add equations and solve for remaining variable. $2x - 6y = 0$ $\underline{-2x - 6y = 16}$ $-3y = 3, y = -1$	Substitute that value into second equation & solve. $6(-y + 5) - 3y = 12$ $6y + 30 - 3y = 12$ $-9y = -18, y = 2$
Substitute that value into original equation. $2x + 3(-1) = -13$ $2x - 3 = -13$ $2x = -10, x = -5$	Substitute that value into an original equation. $6x - 3(2) = 12$ $6x - 6 = 12$ $6x = 18, x = 3$
The solution is: $x = -5, y = -1$ or $(-5,-1)$.	The solution is: $x = 3, y = 2$ or $(3, 2)$.
Validate: $2(-5) - 3(-1) = -13$ $2(-5) + 6(-1) = -16$ $-10 + -3 = -13$ ✓ $-10 - 6 = -16$ ✓	Validate: $-4(3) - 4(2) = -20$ $6(3) - 3(2) = 12$ $-12 - 8 = -20$ ✓ $18 - 6 = 12$ ✓

? CRITICAL THINKING QUESTIONS

1. When solving two simultaneous first-degree equations, what does the solution represent?

2. How do you express this solution (what do you write down)?

3. When is it easier to use to the elimination method for solving simultaneous equations?

4. How would you describe the substitution method for solving simultaneous equations?

5. How can you validate that your answer is correct?

MODULE 32 ADDING RATIONAL EXPRESSIONS

BUILDING UNDERSTANDING

A *rational expression* is the ratio of two polynomials. An example of a rational expression is: $\dfrac{2x+5}{x-1}$. Adding rational expressions is very similar to Adding and Subtracting Fractions (Module 10), except that the numerator and denominator both contain rational expressions rather than numbers: $\dfrac{2x+5}{x-1}+\dfrac{x-3}{x+2}$.

When adding or subtracting rational expressions, it is important to remember that the expressions must have common denominators. With a common denominator, you can then add or subtract the expressions in the numerators.

When adding rational expressions that do not have common denominators, the following formula is a reminder of how to create a common denominator and add the correct product in the numerator.

$$\frac{a}{b}+\frac{c}{d}=\left(\frac{a}{b}\times\frac{d}{d}\right)+\left(\frac{c}{d}\times\frac{b}{b}\right)=\frac{(a\times d)+(b\times c)}{b\times d}$$

METHODOLOGY

Common Denominators

When rational expressions have a **common denominator**:

Step 1	Add and subtract the algebraic expressions in the numerators by combining like terms.
Step 2	Put the resulting expression over the (common) denominator.

For example: $\dfrac{x+3}{x-4}+\dfrac{2x-1}{x-4}=\dfrac{x+3+2x-1}{x-4}=\dfrac{3x+2}{x-4}$

Different Denominators

Adding rational expressions with different denominators requires that the expressions be converted to an equivalent expression with the same denominator. Then the numerators can be added and placed over the common denominator (as described above).

When rational expressions have **different denominators**: $\dfrac{a}{b} + \dfrac{c}{d}$

Step 1	Create a common denominator by multiplying the denominator of one expression by the denominator of the other expression: $(b \times d)$.
Step 2	Since the denominator b was multiplied by expression d, to maintain equivalence, multiply the numerator a by d also: $(a \times d)$.
Step 3	Since the denominator d was multiplied by expression b, to maintain equivalence, multiply the numerator c by b also: $(c \times b)$.
Step 4	Add or subtract the resulting algebraic expressions from Steps 2 & 3. Combine like terms.
Step 5	Place the expression from Step 4 over the (common) denominator.

For example: $\dfrac{a}{b} - \dfrac{c}{d} = \dfrac{2x+5}{x-1} - \dfrac{x-3}{x+2}$

Step 1 $(x-1)(x+2)$ $= x^2 + 2x - x - 2$ $= x^2 + x - 2$ *common denominator*

Step 2 $(2x+5)(x+2)$ $= 2x^2 + 4x + 5x + 10$ $= 2x^2 + 9x + 10$

Step 3 $(x-3)(x-1)$ $= x^2 - x - 3x + 3$ $= x^2 - 4x + 3$

Step 4 $(2x^2 + 9x + 10) - (x^2 - 4x + 3) = 2x^2 - x^2 + 9x + 4x + 10 - 3 = x^2 + 13x + 7$

Step 5 $\dfrac{x^2 + 13x + 7}{x^2 + x - 2}$

THINGS TO REMEMBER

Recall that a **rational number** is a number that can be written in the form $\dfrac{a}{b}$, where a and b are integers and $b \neq 0$. The term *rational* comes from the fact that every rational number can be expressed as the ratio between two integers a and b.

Refer to the following model when adding rational expressions with different denominators.

$$\frac{a}{b} + \frac{c}{d} = \left(\frac{a}{b} \times \frac{d}{d}\right) + \left(\frac{c}{d} \times \frac{b}{b}\right) = \frac{(a \times d) + (b \times c)}{b \times d}$$

Add the following rational expressions:

$$\frac{3x+3}{2x+1}+\frac{-2x+4}{4x-2}=\frac{(3x+3)(4x-2)+(-2x+4)(2x+1)}{(2x+1)(4x-2)}$$

$$=\frac{(12x^2-6x+12x-6)+(-4x^2-2x+8x+4)}{8x^2-4x+4x-2}$$

$$=\frac{12x^2-4x^2-6x+12x-2x+8x-6+4}{8x^2-4x+4x-2}=\frac{8x^2+12x-2}{8x^2-2}$$

$$\frac{-5x+2}{2x+4}+\frac{x-1}{3x-5}=\frac{(-5x+2)(3x-5)+(x-1)(2x+4)}{(2x+4)(3x-5)}$$

$$=\frac{(-15x^2+25x+6x-10)+(2x^2+4x-2x-4)}{6x^2-10x+12x-20}$$

$$=\frac{-15x^2+2x^2+25x+6x+4x-2x-10-4}{6x^2+2x-20}=\frac{-13x^2+33x-14}{6x^2+2x-20}$$

❓ CRITICAL THINKING QUESTIONS

1. What is meant by the phrase *rational expression*?

2. Why is it necessary to create a common denominator when adding rational expressions?

3. By what are you really multiplying a rational expression when you place it over a common denominator?

4. How do you simplify an algebraic expression?

BUILDING UNDERSTANDING

We use measurements as part of our everyday lives. For example:

- We buy gallons of gasoline for our cars
- We drive a certain number of miles to get from city A to city B
- We weigh a certain number of pounds
- We measure square feet of space in a room for new carpeting

We are familiar with units such as: feet, inches, gallons, quarts, and miles. These units are part of the **English Measuring System**. The units of measurement in the English system have been used for a long time, having been commonly accepted for hundreds of years.

Another system of measurement, called the **Metric System**, is used throughout the world. The metric system was developed as a simple system, with units that are related. The relationship between these units involves easy calculations.

While the United States Congress approved the metric system for use, the system is still not widely used in the United States. It is, however, used in many other countries throughout the world. For this reason, it is useful to know how to convert units of measure between the two systems.

By using the equivalent metric units (**conversion factors**), metric values may be calculated for values in English units. The English to metric equivalents are provided in conversion table I below. English values may be calculated for values in metric units by using the conversion equivalents in the metric to English table below (table II).

Table I: English to Metric			Table II: Metric to English		
English Units	=	Metric Units	Metric Units	=	English Units
1 inch	=	2.540 centimeters	1 centimeter	=	0.3937 inches
1 foot	=	0.3048 meters	1 meter	=	3.281 feet
1 mile	=	1.609 kilometer	1 kilometer	=	0.6214 miles
1 quart	=	0.947 liters	1 liter	=	1.057 quarts
1 BTU/hr	=	0.2930 watts	1 watt	=	3.414 BTU/hr

THINGS TO REMEMBER

When performing conversions, always include units in your calculations. Check the units in the end to ensure that you have used the conversion factor correctly.

To Convert from English to Metric units:

$$\text{Metric units} = \text{English value} \times \text{conversion equivalent}$$

$$= \text{English value} \times \frac{\text{Metric equivalent units}}{1\,\text{English unit}}$$

To Convert from Metric to English units:

English units = Metric value × conversion equivalent

$$= \text{Metric value} \times \frac{\text{English equivalent units}}{1 \text{ Metric unit}}$$

 **MODELS**

Converting from English to Metric Units:

convert 4.5 feet to meters:

$$4.5 \text{ feet} \times \frac{0.3048 \text{ meters}}{1 \text{ foot}} = 1.372 \text{ meters}$$

convert 7 quarts to liters:

$$7 \text{ quarts} \times \frac{0.947 \text{ liters}}{1 \text{ quart}} = 6.629 \text{ liters}$$

convert 40 miles/hour to kilometers/hour:

$$\frac{40 \text{ miles}}{1 \text{ hour}} \times \frac{1.609 \text{ kilometers}}{1 \text{ mile}} = \frac{64.36 \text{ kilometers}}{1 \text{ hour}}$$

Converting from Metric to English Units:

convert 120 kilometers to miles:

$$120 \text{ kilometers} \times \frac{0.6214 \text{ miles}}{1 \text{ kilometer}} = 74.57 \text{ miles}$$

convert 100 watts to BTU/hr:

$$100 \text{ watts} \times \frac{3.413 \text{ BTU}/\text{hr}}{1 \text{ watt}} = 341.3 \text{ BTU}/\text{hr}$$

convert 1000 centimeters to inches:

$$1000 \text{ centimeters} \times \frac{0.3937 \text{ inches}}{1 \text{ centimeter}} = 393.7 \text{ inches}$$

? CRITICAL THINKING QUESTIONS

1. What is meant by the term *units*?

2. Why is it useful to be able to perform conversions?

3. Can you convert feet to kilometers? If so, how? If not, why not?

4. Can you convert inches to liters? If so, how? If not, why not?

5. How does checking units help you to make sure that your conversion was performed correctly?

BUILDING UNDERSTANDING

A *base* is a whole number that is made *the* fundamental number of a number system, which is then raised to various powers to produce the major counting units. While base 10 is by far the most common and familiar base used in our society and daily lives, it is not the only number system.

In **base 10** there are *ten* numbers (0, 1, 2, 3, 4, 5, 6, 7, 8, 9). When counting in base 10, after reaching the number 9, there are no more single-digit numbers so the next number becomes a two-digit number, 10, with the right-most digit starting over at zero and the second column number starting at 1. After 99, a three digit number, 100, is the next number. After 999, a four-digit number, 1000, is next.

An analogous situation is true with numbers in other bases. For example, in **base 2** there are *two* numbers (0 and 1), and in **base 5** there are *five* numbers (0, 1, 2, 3, 4). When counting in base 5, after reaching the number 4, there are no more single-digit numbers so the next number becomes a two-digit number, 10, with the right-most digit starting over at zero and the second column number is one. After 44, a three-digit number, 100 is the next number. After 444, a four-digit number, 1000, is next.

With a number in base 10, the right-most digit is the "1's digit" and the next digit to the left is the "10's digit" and the next digit to the left is the "100's digit" and so on. Notice the pattern that is occurring here. The right-most digit is a single-digit number times 10^0, while the next digit is a single-digit number times 10^1, the next digit is a single-digit number times 10^2, and so on. For example:

$$528 = 8 + 20 + 500$$
$$= (8 \times 1) + (2 \times 10) + (5 \times 100)$$
$$= (8 \times 10^0) + (2 \times 10^1) + (5 \times 10^2)$$

$$384 = 4 + 80 + 300$$
$$= (4 \times 1) + (8 \times 10) + (3 \times 100)$$
$$= (4 \times 10^0) + (8 \times 10^1) + (3 \times 10^2)$$

METHODOLOGY

Converting from Other Bases to Base 10:

Step 1	Identify the current base, b, of the number. *Each digit in the number will be multiplied by the base, b, raised to a power. Work first with the right-most digit and move left.*
Step 2	Multiply the right-most digit by the base, b, raised to the zero power (or 1).
Step 3	Multiply the second digit from the right by the base, b, raised to the first power.
Step 4	Multiply the third digit from the right by the base, b, raised to the second power.
Step 5	Multiply the fourth digit from the right by the base, b, raised to the third power. *Continue in this manner until all the digits have been multiplied by the base raised to a power.*
Step 6	Sum all the products from the previous steps to obtain the equivalent base 10 number.

Common notation is: number$_{base}$. For example 231 in base 4 is written as: 231_4

The number of a base is also the number of single-digit numbers that may be used in that base. For example, in base 4, there are four numbers (0 through 3); in base 6, there are six numbers (0 through 5).

Within a particular base, the number of the base and those single-digit numbers greater than the number of the base (the numbers we are used to using in base 10) simply do not exist. For example, the numbers 4, 5, 6, 7, 8, and 9 do not exist in the base 4 number system which only uses the numbers 0, 1, 2, and 3.

When converting a number to base 10, start with the *right-most digit* multiplied by the base to the zero power (the right-most digit is always multiplied by 1, which is the base raised to the zero power). The table below summarizes which power is associated with which digit.

base^3 × d	base^2 × c	base^1 × b	base^0 × a
fourth digit, d	third digit, c	second digit, b	right-most digit, a

 MODELS

Change the number in the given base to its equivalent number in base 10:

$34_6 = (6^0 \times 4) + (6^1 \times 3)$
$\qquad = (1 \times 4) + (6 \times 3)$
$\qquad = 4 + 18$
$\qquad = 22$

$23_5 = (5^0 \times 3) + (5^1 \times 2)$
$\qquad = (1 \times 3) + (5 \times 2)$
$\qquad = 3 + 10$
$\qquad = 13$

$111_4 = (4^0 \times 1) + (4^1 \times 1) + (4^2 \times 1)$
$\qquad = (1 \times 1) + (4 \times 1) + (16 \times 1)$
$\qquad = 1 + 4 + 16$
$\qquad = 21$

$78_9 = (9^0 \times 8) + (9^1 \times 7)$
$\qquad = (1 \times 8) + (9 \times 7)$
$\qquad = 8 + 63$
$\qquad = 71$

$1234_5 = (5^0 \times 4) + (5^1 \times 3) + (5^2 \times 2) + (5^3 \times 1)$
$\qquad = (1 \times 4) + (5 \times 3) + (25 \times 2) + (125 \times 1)$
$\qquad = 1 + 15 + 50 + 125$
$\qquad = 191$

$10101_2 = (2^0 \times 1) + (2^1 \times 0) + (2^2 \times 1) + (2^3 \times 0) + (2^4 \times 1)$
$\qquad = (1 \times 1) + (2 \times 0) + (4 \times 1) + (8 \times 0) + (16 \times 1)$
$\qquad = 1 + 0 + 4 + 0 + 16$
$\qquad = 21$

1. What numbers are there in a base 7 number system?

2. Why is it not possible to have the number 22 in a base 2 number system?

3. In a base 6 number system what is the next number after 55? Why?

4. Without doing any calculations, which number is bigger, 100_4 or 100_5? How do you know?

5. It can be said that time is measured in a base 60 system. Considering that 1 hour = 60 minutes and 1 minute = 60 seconds, we can give a time of 3 hours, 14 minutes and 52 seconds as $3 \times 60^2 + 14 \times 60^1 + 52 \times 60^0$ seconds or 3:14:52. Applying what you have learned in this module, can you covert that number to base 10? Why or why not? Would doing so be at all useful? Explain your answer.

MODULE 35 LOGARITHMS

BUILDING UNDERSTANDING

In short, *logarithms* are *exponents*. Logarithms are a tool used to simplify calculations involving the multiplication and division of numbers raised to a power.

Consider the following expression: $x = b^y$ The *logarithm* of a positive number (x) to a certain base (b) is the exponent (y) to which that base must be raised to give the number (x).

For example, $16 = 2 \times 2 \times 2 \times 2 = 2^4$, can be read "4 is exponent or logarithm with respect to the base 2."

Statements that are written in *exponential form* can also be written in *logarithmic form*.

In general, $b^a = x$ is the same as $\log_b x = a$

Common Logarithms

Common logarithms are logarithms whose base is 10. Therefore, the common logarithm of a number is the exponent to which 10 must be raised to yield the number. With common logarithms, no base is indicated when writing the expression in logarithmic form (i.e., $\log = \log_{10}$) Therefore, when you see $\log$, know that the implied base is 10.

Exponential form	**Logarithmic form**	
$4^2 = 16$	$\log_4 16 = 2$	*4 to what power equals 16? 2*
$2^6 = 64$	$\log_2 64 = 6$	*2 to what power equals 64? 6*
$10^3 = 1000$	$\log 1000 = 3$	*10 to what power equals 1000? 3*

Natural Logarithms

Natural logarithms are logarithms (exponents) whose base is called e (e is approximately 2.71 828). Natural logarithms are written beginning with $\ln$. *Note:* $\ln e^x = x$.

METHODOLOGY

Multiplication by the Use of Logarithms:

The logarithm of the **product** of two numbers is obtained by **adding** the logarithms of the two numbers.

$\log(a \times b) = \log a + \log b$

$\ln(a \times b) = \ln a + \ln b$

For example:

$\log(10^2 \times 10^4) = \log 10^2 + \log 10^4 = 2 + 4 = 6$

$\ln(e^{-3} \times e^{-2}) = \ln e^{-3} + \ln e^{-2} = -3 + -2 = -5$

Division by the Use of Logarithms:

The logarithm of the **quotient** of two numbers is obtained by **subtracting** the logarithm of the divisor from the logarithm of the dividend.

$$\log(a \div b) = \log a - \log b$$

$$\ln(a \div b) = \ln a - \ln b$$

For example:

$$\log(10^2 \div 10^4) = \log 10^2 - \log 10^4 = 2 - 4 = -2$$

$$\ln(e^{-3} \div e^{-2}) = \ln e^{-3} - \ln e^{-2} = -3 - (-2) = -1$$

 THINGS TO REMEMBER

Note: the following rules of logarithms are true for $b > 0$ and $b \neq 1$, $a > 0$, and $b > 0$.

$\log = \log_{10}$	if no subscript appears, the base is assumed to be 10
$\log_b 1 = 0$	*any number, except 0, raised to the zero power equals one:* $\log_5 1 = 0$
$\log_b b = 1$	*a number raised to the first power is equal to itself*
$\log_b(a \times b) = \log_b a + \log_b b$	$\ln_e(a \times b) = \ln_e a + \ln_e b$
$\log_b(a \div b) = \log_b a - \log_b b$	$\ln_e(a \div b) = \ln_e a - \ln_e b$
$\log_b b^p = p$	*b to what power of b equals p? the answer is p*
$\ln_e e^p = p$	*e to what power of e equals p? the answer is p*

 MODELS

Perform the following calculations:

$$\log(10^4 \times 10^3) = \log(10^4) + \log(10^3) = 4 + 3 = 7$$

$$\log(10^5 \times 10^{-2}) = \log(10^5) + \log(10^{-2}) = 5 + (-2) = 3$$

$$\log(10^{-6} \times 10^{-5}) = \log(10^{-6}) + \log(10^{-5}) = -6 + (-5) = -11$$

$$\log(10^0 \div 10^1) = \log(10^0) - \log(10^1) = 0 - 1 = -1$$

$$\log(10^3 \div 10^{-2}) = \log(10^3) - \log(10^{-2}) = 3 - (-2) = 5$$

$$\ln(e^4 \times e^2) = \ln(e^4) + \ln(e^2) = 4 + 2 = 6$$

$$\ln(e^{-1} \times e^4) = \ln(e^{-1}) + \ln(e^4) = -1 + 4 = 3$$

$$\ln(e^{-4} \times e^4) = \ln(e^{-4}) + \ln(e^4) = -4 + 4 = 0$$

$$\ln(e^2 \div e^{-1}) = \ln(e^2) - \ln(e^{-1}) = 2 - (-1) = 3$$

$$\ln(e^4 \div e^3) = \ln(e^4) - \ln(e^{-3}) = 4 - 3 = 1$$

Math and Graphing Skills

1. How does the statement $x = b^y$ help to explain what a logarithm is?

2. What is a common logarithm? Provide an example along with your explanation.

3. How do you convert $5^3 = 125$ into logarithmic form?

4. Why is $\log_b 1$ equal to zero, no matter what the base, b, is?

5. How does a natural logarithm differ from a common logarithm?

6. How do the rules for multiplying and dividing logarithms relate to the rules of exponents?

TABLES AND STATISTICS

 BUILDING UNDERSTANDING

A *table* (of data) is an arrangement of related facts, figures, and values presented in an orderly sequence, usually in rows and columns for convenience of reference. In this module you will be asked questions concerning the data in a table.

The data in a table is given meaning from the title and the labels associated with the rows and columns. Typically, the column labels represent the variables that have been measured (e.g., age, annual income, year in school, phone number, etc.) and row labels identify the objects associated with these measurements (e.g., people, states, organizations, etc.)

Some of the questions about data in a table require you to use your observation skills. Examples of these types of questions include, Who is the youngest person? What is the minimum income? Who has the second highest I.Q?

Some of the questions require you to use some basic *statistics*; specifically, finding the mean and median values of a column of data.

Consider the following table of information concerning a publisher's book inventory in a warehouse. The column headings refer to pricing, inventory quantity, and location by aisle number for three books, the titles of which are found in the row labels.

Warehouse Book Inventory	Price	Quantity	Aisle #
Book #1 – *Foundations of Learning*	$40	538 books	2
Book #2 – *Learning Assessment Journal*	$12	695 books	5
Book #3 – *Math & Graphing Skills*	$20	327 books	3

THINGS TO REMEMBER

The *maximum value* with respect to an item of measurement or piece of information is the largest value within the specified column. For example, in the table above, the largest inventory quantity is for the *Learning Assessment Journal*, since:

695 books > 538 books > 327 books

The *minimum value* with respect to an item of measurement or piece of information is the smallest value within the specified column. For example, in the table above, the smallest or lowest price for a book is for *Math & Graphing Skills*, since:

$12 < $20 < $40

The *range* of the values for an item of measurement or piece of information is the distance between the maximum value and the minimum value in the specified column. The range of prices for the three books in the table above is: $40 – $12 = $28

Range = maximum value – minimum value

The *mean* (often referred to as the "average") of a set of values is calculated by taking the sum of all the values and dividing the sum by the number of values. The mean price for the three books is: ($40 + $12 + $20) ÷ 3 = $72 ÷ 3 = **$24**

$$\text{Mean} = \frac{\text{(sum of the values)}}{\text{(the number of values)}}$$

The *median* value from a set of ordered values is the one that has half of the values above it and half below it. When the set of values is an *odd number*, the median is the *middle value*. When the set of values is *even*, the median is the *mean of the two middle values*. The median price of the three books is **$20**, the middle of the three ordered values: {$12, $20, $40}.

 MODELS

Consider the table of data below and answer the following questions.

Names	Income (in dollars)	IQ (in points)	Age (in years)
Brett	5,000	129	19
Sarah	4,000	122	23
Lisa	6,000	128	22
Tony	7,000	126	25
Rachel	3,000	125	21

1. What is the mean income? (5,000 + 4,000 + 6,000 + 7,000 + 3,000) ÷ 5 = $25,000 ÷ 5 = **$5,000**

2. What is the median age? The ages in order are {19, 21, 22, 23, 25}. The middle value is **22 years**.

3. What is the range of I.Q.'s? Range = maximum value – minimum value = 129 – 122 = **7 points**

4. Who is the youngest person? The smallest value for age is 19, belonging to **Brett**.

5. Who has the larger income, Brett or Lisa? Since $6,000 > $5,000 **Lisa** has the larger income.

? CRITICAL THINKING QUESTIONS

1. In general terms, how are tables of data typically arranged? What goes in the rows versus what goes in the columns?

2. Must information in a table always be presented as numbers? Why?

3. Can the range ever be greater than the maximum value? Why?

4. Can the mean and the median of a set of values ever be the same? If so, give an example. If not, explain why not.

5. How do you determine the median value from a set of six values?

BUILDING UNDERSTANDING

An ***arithmetic sequence*** is a series of numbers in which, after the first element, each element is found by adding (or subtracting) a constant number from the previous element.

An example of an arithmetic sequence is 13, 17, 21, 25,... 53.

The sequence starts at 13 and progresses by adding 4 to each previous element. In other words, there is a ***common difference*** of 4 between each element in the sequence. The ***number of intervals*** in the sequence may be calculated by taking the difference between the last and first element and dividing it by the common difference: (53 − 13) ÷ 4 = 10. The ***number of elements*** in the sequence may be calculated by adding one to the number of intervals: 10 + 1 = 11.

THINGS TO REMEMBER

For an Arithmetic Sequence *a*, *b*, *c*, ..., *n*

- The *common difference* between element is equal to *b* − *a*.

- The *number of elements* in the sequence is calculated by:

$$\frac{(\text{starting point} - \text{ending point})}{(\text{common difference})} + 1 = \frac{(n-a)}{(b-a)} + 1$$

- The *next element* in the sequence after *n* is calculated by:

$$\text{next element} = \text{last element} + \text{common difference} = n + (b - a)$$

MODELS

For the following sequences, determine the number of elements in the sequence and the next number in the sequence.

Sequence	Number of Elements	Next Element
5, 8, 11, ..., 35	$\frac{(35-5)}{(8-5)} + 1 = \frac{30}{3} + 1 = 10 + 1 = 11$	35 + (8 − 5) = 35 + 3 = 38
10, 5, 0, −5, ..., −25	$\frac{(-25-10)}{(5-10)} + 1 = \frac{-35}{-5} + 1 = 7 + 1 = 8$	−25 + (5 − 10) = −25 + (−5) = −30
−10, −6, −2, ..., 26	$\frac{(26-(-10))}{(-6-(-10))} + 1 = \frac{36}{4} + 1 = 9 + 1 = 10$	26 + (−6 − (−10)) = 26 + 4 = 30

1. What makes a sequence an *arithmetic sequence*?

2. What does the term *common difference* mean? How is it calculated?

3. How is the common difference used to determine the number elements in a sequence and the next element in a sequence?

4. Why are there fewer intervals than elements in a sequence?

BUILDING UNDERSTANDING

The *perimeter* of a two-dimensional shape is the measurement around it. In a similar manner, the *circumference* of a circle represents the distance around the circle.

The *area* of a two-dimensional shape is the measure of the bounded region in a plane.

THINGS TO REMEMBER

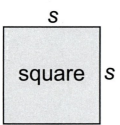

Area = s^2
Perimeter = $4 \times s$
s = length of any side

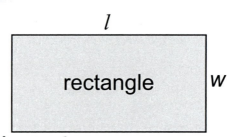

Area = $l \times w$
Perimeter = $(2 \times l) + (2 \times w)$
l = length of a side, w = width of a side

circle

r

Area = $\pi \times r^2$
Circumference = $2 \times \pi \times r$
r = radius of the circle

triangle

Area = $\frac{1}{2} b \times h$
b = length of base
h = height

b

h

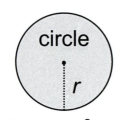

Area = $b \times h$
b = length of base
h = height

parallelogram

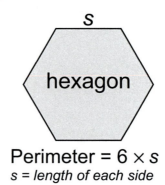

hexagon

Perimeter = $6 \times s$
s = length of each side

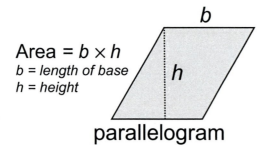

Perimeter = $8 \times s$
s = length of each side

octagon

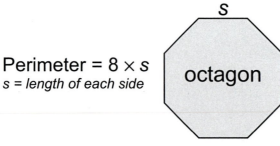

MODELS

Below is an example of the type of problem you will see on the computer. You will see a geometric figure and be asked to calculate its perimeter or area.

It is important that you (1) use the correct equation or formula, and (2) read the graph accurately to obtain the correct measures for length, width, height, etc., as required by the formula.

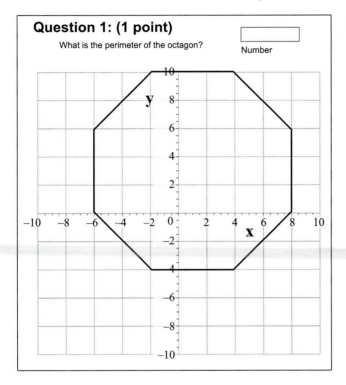

Question 1: (1 point)

What is the perimeter of the octagon?

Number [   ]

Calculate the perimeter of the octagon in the diagram to the left:

Perimeter = 8 × s
s = 4 − (−2) = 6
Perimeter = 8 × 6 = **48 units**

Additional Examples:

Calculate the area of a triangle where the base is 40 units and the height is 60 units:

Area = (1/2) × 40 × 60
= (1/2) × 2400
= **1200 square units**

Calculate the area of a parallelogram with a base of 5 inches and a height of 7 inches:

Area = b × h
= 5 × 7 = **35 square inches**

? CRITICAL THINKING QUESTIONS

1. If measurements are given in feet, what are the final units for the perimeter and area of a rectangle?

2. What is the difference between a hexagon and an octagon?

3. What is the difference between a parallelogram and a rectangle?

4. What is the difference between the perimeter and area of a two-dimensional shape?

5. What measurements do you need to make in order to determine the perimeters of a hexagon, octagon, and square?

6. How do you determine the height of parallelograms and triangles?

BUILDING UNDERSTANDING

The word *set* is used in many different contexts. For our purposes, a *set* is *a well-defined collection of objects or elements*. By "well-defined," we mean that one should be able to determine whether or not an object or element belongs to a given collection.

The following are examples of sets: the set of even integers, the set of days in the year 2009, and the set of states that begin with the letter "M." The collection of "good students" in your class, or the collection of "computer experts" in a company are generally not considered sets because they are not well-defined. A set could be made by changing "good students" to all students with a GPA of 3.0 or better. Similarly, we can define "computer expert" as someone with a degree in computer science. This allows us to define that set.

The sets that you will see in the computer module that accompanies this book are clearly defined. What you will see on the computer will look similar to the diagram at right. This is an example of a **Venn diagram**.

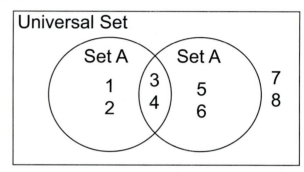

A *universal set* is an all-inclusive set that contains all elements of interest. The universal sets in the computer module have two circles (labeled **Set A** and **Set B**) with integers in them. The circles overlap with an area of *intersection* between the two sets. In the Universal Set above, the intersection of sets A & B includes the integers 3 and 4. Note that there are also integers outside of sets A and B that are contained within the Universal Set.

THINGS TO REMEMBER

Set Operations

The *union* of two sets (A & B) is represented by the set of all elements that belong to or are in both sets. Symbolically, the union of set A and set B is written: $A \cup B$.

The *intersection* of two sets (A & B) is represented by the set of elements that are common to both sets. Symbolically, the intersection of set A and set B is written: $A \cap B$.

The *complement* of a set (A) is represented by the set of all elements that are not in found in that set (A). Symbolically, the complement of set A is written: A'.

Union of sets A and B	Intersection of sets A and B	Complement of set A
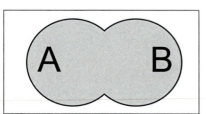	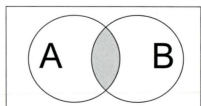	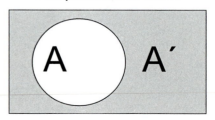

Answer the following questions with respect to the Universal Set below.

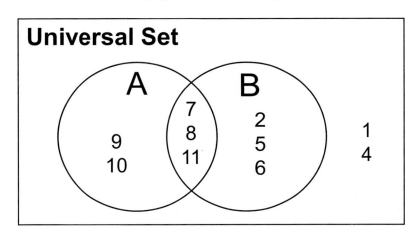

Which elements are in set B?

{7, 8, 11, 2, 5, 6}

Which elements are in the union of sets A & B?

{9, 10, 7, 8, 11, 2, 5, 6}

Which elements are in the intersection of sets A & B?

{7, 8, 11}

Which elements are in the complement of set B?   {1, 4, 9, 10}

Which elements are in the complement of A ∪ B?   {1, 4}

Which elements are in the complement of A ∩ B?   {9, 10, 2, 5, 6, 1, 4}

? CRITICAL THINKING QUESTIONS

1. What is meant by the term ***universal set***? Does a universal set exclude any elements?

2. What does it mean when we say "the elements contained in a set" and call that ***set A***?

3. What is the difference between the union and the intersection of two sets?

4. How would you draw a picture of a universal set where the shaded area represents the complement of the union of set A and set B?

BUILDING UNDERSTANDING

A ***cardinal number*** is any number used in *counting* or in showing *how many*. Examples of cardinal numbers include: two, forty, 35, 267, etc. In comparison, an ***ordinal number*** is any number used to *indicate order* (e.g., second, ninth, 25th) in a particular series.

In a set of numbers, the number of members contained in that set is called its cardinal number or ***cardinality***. For example, if set A = {4, –6, 3.5, 212}, the cardinality of set A is 4 because there are four numbers or members contained in the set.

THINGS TO REMEMBER

1. The cardinality of a set is determined by counting the number of members or elements in that set.

2. When dealing with the cardinality of more than one set of numbers, it is important to know the vocabulary associated with the *relationship between sets* so that you can correctly count and determine the appropriate cardinality. The most common terms include ***intersection, union***, and ***complement*** of sets. Refer to the previous module on sets for a review of these terms.

MODELS

Consider the following sets: A = {3, 7, 2, 5, 10}   B = {–1, 20, 5}   C = {8}

1. What is the cardinality of each individual set?

   set A: cardinality is **5**   set B: cardinality is **3**   set C: cardinality is **1**

2. What is the cardinality of the union of sets A, B, and C?

   A $\cup$ B $\cup$ C = {–1, 2, 3, 5, 7, 8, 10, 20}, cardinality is **8**

3. What is the cardinality of the intersection of set A and set B?

   A $\cap$ B = {5}, cardinality is **1**

? CRITICAL THINKING QUESTIONS

1. What is difference between a *cardinal* number and an *ordinal* number?

2. What does it mean when we say the "cardinality" of a set?

3. Is it possible to have a cardinality of zero? Explain.